Y0-BRN-890

VOL **10** HIP-JAD
791–878

FUNK & WAGNALLS **new**
ENCYCLOPEDIA
OF SCIENCE

FUNK & WAGNALLS, INC.

HOW TO USE FUNK & WAGNALLS NEW ENCYCLOPEDIA OF SCIENCE

Volumes 1 through 21 have information printed on the front covers, spine, and title pages that make it easy to find the articles you want to read.
- Volume numbers are printed in all three places in Volumes 1 through 21.
- Letter breaks — $\frac{COL}{DIA}$ — are printed in all three places in Volumes 1 through 21. The letters above the line are the first three letters of the first article title in the volume. The letters below the line are the first three letters of the last article title in the volume.
- Page breaks — $\frac{351}{438}$ — are printed on the spines and title pages of Volumes 1 through 21. They provide the page numbers of the first and last text pages in the volume.

Articles are arranged alphabetically by title in Volumes 1 through 21. Most titles are printed in **BOLD-FACE CAPITAL** letters. Some titles are printed in even larger letters.
- Some titles are not article titles, but refer you to the actual article title. Within articles you will find *See* or *See also* other article names for further information. All of these references to other articles are called cross-references.
- Most article titles are followed by a phonetic pronunciation. Use the Pronunciation Guide on page vi of Volume 1 to learn the correct pronunciation of the article title.
- At the end of most articles are two sets of initials. The first set identifies the person who wrote the article. The second set identifies the special consultant who checked the article for accuracy. All of these people are listed by their initials and full names and position on pages v and vi of Volume 1.
- ◣ This symbol at the end of an article indicates that there is a project based on the subject of the article in the Projects, Bibliography & Index volume. The project is found under its article title, and all of the project article titles are arranged alphabetically on pages 1 through 64 of the Projects, Bibliography & Index volume.

The Projects, Bibliography & Index Volume contains three sections. Each is an essential part of the encyclopedia.
- Projects based on articles in the encyclopedia are found in the first section. Each is both entertaining and educational. Each is designed for use by a student and for parental participation if desired.
- Bibliography reading lists in the second section list books under general scientific categories that are also titles of major articles. Each book listed is marked with either a YA (Young Adult) or J (Juvenile) reading level indicator. YA generally applies to readers at the junior high level or higher. J applies to readers at grade levels below junior high school.
- Index entries for all article titles plus many subjects that are not article titles are found in the third section. Instructions on using the Index are found at the start of the Index section in the Projects, Bibliography & Index volume.

HIPPARCHUS (about 160–about 126 BC) Hipparchus (hi pär′ kəs) was a Greek astronomer. All that we know about him comes from the writings of Ptolemy. Ptolemy tells us that Hipparchus built an observatory at Rhodes. He is the earliest systematic astronomer we know about. He discovered the precession of the equinoxes and catalogued more than a thousand stars. Hipparchus must have been a brilliant mathematician as well as an outstanding scientist. He invented trigonometry and worked out the distances of the sun and moon from earth. He also used a system of latitude and longitude to show where places on earth are. *See also* EQUINOX; PTOLEMY; TRIGONOMETRY. C.M./D.G.F.

HIPPOCRATES (about 470–about 377 BC) Hippocrates (hi pòk′ rə tēz) was a Greek doctor. He was born on the island of Cos. He is called ''the father of medicine.'' Modern medical students make a promise to be ethical in their work. This is called the Hippocratic Oath.

Hippocrates is supposed to have written a large number of books. Most of these were probably written by other doctors working on Cos at the same time. They are known as the Hippocratic School. Some of the descriptions of diseases in these books are very clear and accurate. The diseases can be recognized today. No other medical books as scientific as these were written until modern times. C.M./D.G.F.

HIPPOPOTAMUS (hip′ ə pät′ ə məs) Hippopotamus is the name given to two species of huge land mammals native to central and western Africa. Although its name comes from two Greek words meaning ''water horse,'' the hippopotamus is more closely related to the pig than to the horse. The river hippopotamus (*Hippopotamus amphibius*) is

The river hippopotamus is also called the great African hippopotamus. To keep cool, it spends almost the whole day with most of its body under water. It is able to do that because its eyes, ears, and nostrils all stick out from the tip of its head.
H. Reinhard/Bruce Coleman, Inc.

also called the great African hippopotamus. It has a large body, short legs, and feet with webbed toes. It may grow to be 5 m [16.5 ft] long and 1.5 m [5 ft] tall at the shoulder. The largest weigh close to 3,000 kg [6,600 lb]. The eyes, ears, and nostrils all stick out from the top of the head. This allows the animal to see, hear, and breathe while most of its body is under water. The hippopotamus has special oil glands to keep the grayish skin moist. The oil is sometimes red, giving rise to the incorrect belief that the animal sweats blood.

The hippopotamus has large, curved teeth. Its canine teeth are enlarged into tusks which may be 60 cm [2 ft] long. The hippopotamus is a good swimmer and, on land, can run as fast as 48 km [30 mi] per hour. Hippopotamuses roam in herds of as many as 30 animals, spending most of the day in the water. At night, hippopotamuses leave the water and graze on land, often causing great destruction to cultivated crops. An average hippopotamus eats about 60 kg [132 lb] of food each day.

A female hippopotamus first mates when she is five or six years old. After a gestation period of about eight months, she gives birth to one calf. The newborn calf may weigh as much as 50 kg [110 lb]. The calf is able to swim almost immediately. It nurses underwater, surfacing every few minutes for air. Hippopotamuses live for about 30 years.

The pygmy hippopotamus (*Choeropsis liberiensis*) is much smaller and darker than the river hippopotamus. It weighs about 230 kg [506 lb] and is about 1.8 m [6 ft] long. It stands only 75 cm [2.5 ft] tall at the shoulder. This animal spends relatively little time in the water, and usually wanders through forests and grasslands.

Hippopotamuses are widely hunted for their hides, meat, and ivory tusks. Although protected by law in most places, these animals are often killed illegally. The pygmy hippopotamus is an endangered species and may soon be extinct.   A.J.C./J.J.M.

HISTOLOGY (his täl′ ə jē) Histology is the microscopic study of plant and animal tissue. Tissue is a group of similar cells that work together to perform a specific function. (*See* TISSUE.) Histologists examine tissue to learn about its structure, functions, and properties. A biopsy is the examination of a specific tissue sample taken from a living organism. Biopsies give scientists valuable information about disease processes. An autopsy includes histological examination after an animal's death and helps doctors and scientists learn more about disease and the cause of death.

Histology as a science progressed slowly until the 19th century, when the compound microscope began to acquire a form resembling its current one. (*See* MICROSCOPE.) The microtome, an instrument for slicing thin portions of tissue, was developed during the same period by a Czech doctor and enabled histologists to study tissue more accurately than before. In 1907 the American biologist Ross Granville Harrison discovered that living tissues could be grown outside the organ from which the tissues were taken. That process is called culturing. The electron microscope, developed in the early 20th century, and the electron scanning microscope, introduced in 1968, made possible great advancements in the study of tissue. (*See* ELECTRON MICROSCOPE.)

HIVES   Hives is the name given to an allergic disorder of the skin. This condition is characterized by the sudden appearance of small raised areas on the skin. Itching and redness usually accompany the appearance of the bumps. In some cases hives disappear quickly, whereas in other cases they linger. Hives commonly appear on covered areas of the skin, but rarely on the palms, soles, or scalp. The disorder is attributed to an allergic reaction, which occurs rapidly after the allergic person eats, breathes, or comes into contact with the substance that causes the allergy. (*See* ALLERGY.)

Many foods cause allergic hives, but not everyone is allergic to these foods. In the same way, some medications can cause hives, and even animal fur and dust can bring on hives. Different fabrics, plants, pollen, and environmental substances can cause hives. There are so many possible reasons for hives that, if they persist or recur frequently, a doctor should examine the patient to determine the best treatment.

HOFMANN, AUGUST (1818–1892) August Hofmann (hōf′ män) was a German chemist. He was born in Giessen. In 1845 he became the director of the Royal College of Chemistry in London, where he stayed until 1864. He made many important discoveries in organic chemistry. He is famous for the Hofmann degradation reaction. This is a way of changing an organic compound by removing a carbon atom from each molecule. Hofmann developed aniline dyes from coal products. These are called Hofmann violets. He also discovered formaldehyde and styrene.   C.M./D.G.F.

HOFSTADTER, ROBERT (1915–) Robert Hofstadter is an American physicist. He was born in New York City. Hofstadter joined the faculty of Stanford University in 1950. His work in measuring the size and shape of both the proton and the neutron yielded the most precise information about those particles that had been available up to that time. Hofstadter used the linear accelerator at Stanford and a scattering machine that he designed himself. (*See* ACCELERATOR.) As a result of Hofstadter's work, scientists now know that both the proton and the neutron consist of a dense, pointlike core of mesons surrounded by two layers of meson clouds. These two layers blend together. (*See* NEUTRON; PARTICLE PHYSICS; PROTON.) Hofstadter was awarded the Nobel Prize in Physics in 1961.

HOLLY FAMILY The holly (häl′ ē) family includes 295 species of evergreen trees and shrubs with shiny green leaves and red fruits. The name probably comes from the fact that these popular Christmas plants were once thought to be holy trees. They have alternate, simple leaves, and flowers clustered in the axils. Most members of the holly family are dioecious. That is, each plant has either male flowers or female flowers, but not both.

The American holly (*Ilex opaca*) may grow to a height of 30 m [100 ft]. Its red fruits are called berries, but they are actually drupes. The fruits are poisonous and grow only on the female trees (with the pistillate flowers). English holly (*Ilex aquifolium*) is a popular shrub that is often grown with hawthorn in hedges. The leaves of a South American species, *Ilex paraguariensis*, are brewed to make a beverage called maté.

The wood from members of the holly family is very hard. It is used to make musical instruments and furniture.   A.J.C./M.H.S.

European holly, species *Ilex aquifolium*.

HOLLYHOCK (häl′ ē häk′) Hollyhock (*Althaea rosea*) is a herbaceous plant belonging to the mallow family. Though native to China, it is widely cultivated in the United States for its spikes of colorful red, pink, purple, or yellow flowers. The large (7.5 cm

[3 in]) blossoms grow from the axils near the top of a thick stem. This stem with its spike of flowers may grow to be as tall as 2.7 m [9 ft]. The leaves are usually large, hairy, and heart-shaped with five to seven lobes. Though most varieties are perennial, some are annual or biennial. *See also* INFLORESCENCE; MALLOW FAMILY.   A.J.C./M.H.S.

HOLMIUM (hōl′ mē əm) Holmium (Ho) is a bright silvery metallic element. The atomic number of holmium is 67 and its atomic weight is 164.93. It melts at 1,474°C [2,685°F] and boils at 2,695°C [4,883°F]. Its relative density is 8.8. It is one of the rare earth group of metals and is obtained from the mineral monazite. Holmium was discovered by the Swiss chemist J. L. Soret in 1878. No important uses have yet been discovered for the metal.   M.E./J.R.W.

HOLOGRAPHY (hō läg′ rə fē) Holography is a technique for viewing and recording a photographic image in three dimensions. The image can be recorded on a photographic plate, called a hologram. The word *hologram* means "total message."

A hologram appears to be a complex pattern of stripes and whorls. But, when the hologram is illuminated by a laser beam, the light is reconstructed into a three-dimensional image of the object that was photographed.

In photography, light reflected from an object forms an image on film that is exposed to it. The film is then chemically processed, and can be used to make a photograph. An ordinary photograph presents a flat image in two dimensions—height and width. (*See* PHOTOGRAPHY.) Holography creates a third dimension—depth. The image changes when seen from slightly different angles. An observer must refocus his eyes to see the foreground and the background. He is able to see around and behind the object viewed.

Holography was invented in 1948 by the Hungarian-born scientist Dennis Gabor, who was working in England. Gabor received the Nobel Prize for Physics in 1971. Gabor wanted to use holography to improve the capabilities of the electron microscope. His original application of holography did not prove to be practical.

In the 1960s, the field of holography was expanded by the invention of the laser. Emmett Leith and Juris Upatnieks, two scientists working in the United States, achieved remarkable results by applying laser beams to the process of holography. A laser is a nar-

This diagram shows how a hologram, a three-dimensional image, is recorded and reproduced.

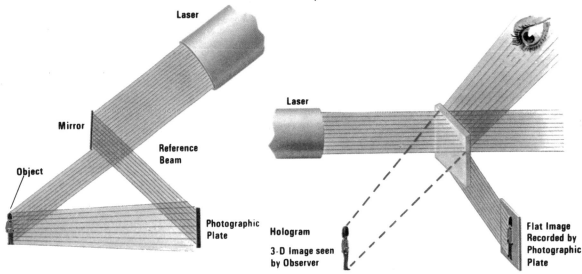

Laser

Mirror

Object

Reference Beam

Photographic Plate

Laser

Hologram

3-D Image seen by Observer

Flat Image Recorded by Photographic Plate

The photograph on the left shows some of the optical equipment — including a laser — used to create a hologram. On the right is a hologram called "Future Memories."

row, concentrated beam of light. (*See* LASER.) The work of Leith and Upatnieks opened the way for many research applications. The technique is widely used as a method of optical image formation, and is also used for recording acoustical and radio waves.

How holography works　To create a three-dimensional image by holography, light reflected from a source must itself be photographed. The light waves are photographed when frozen for a very small fraction of a second. The wave pattern can then be reconstructed to show the same three-dimensional character of the solid object from which the light is reflected.

　In a darkened room, a beam of laser light is directed at an object. Part of the beam strikes the object and reflects from the object to be recorded on photographic film or a plate. This is called the object wave. The other part of the beam bypasses the object and reflects off a mirror standing near the object, directly to the recording plate. This is called the reference wave. What is actually recorded on the photographic plate is the sum of light from the object wave and the reference wave. The combined waves interfere with each other, creating light and dark patches, called an interference pattern. (*See* INTERFERENCE.)

　The photographic plate or film, when developed, is called a hologram. The image on the hologram does not resemble the object at all. But, when laser light is directed onto the transparent hologram, it causes the laser beam to be split up into different beams. One of the beams produces a reconstructed flat image of the original object, which can be recorded on film. Another beam creates a three-dimensional image, which is reconstructed in space directly behind the original object.

Applications　Holography is a relatively expensive procedure for solving optical image problems. Lasers are complex and costly equipment, and long exposures are required to reconstruct images. The technique, however, has many commercial applications.

　In conventional microscopy, the microscope provides high magnification powers, but with a very limited depth of focus. By using a laser beam, a moving object can actually be frozen in time and recorded on a hologram. The approach has been successful in examining microorganisms three-dimensionally.

The technique has been useful in computer storage systems by providing unique optical memory banks. Large volumes of binary data can be reconstructed from an array of small holograms.

Holography has also been used to record the wave patterns of vibrating instruments such as the violin. It has been used to measure the strain of certain materials under stress. An image reconstructed by holographic interferometry can record the waves of compression generated by a high-speed rifle bullet. (*See* INTERFEROMETER.)

Artists and photographers have used holograms to create unusual artistic works. Photographers are especially interested in creating 3-D realism in photography, and new cameras and photographic materials have been developed to achieve this end.

The Space Graph employs holographic techniques. The instrument allows a person to see an object as it appears from several different viewpoints. The viewer can look over, under, and around an image simply by moving his head.

The Space Graph may be useful in seismic data analysis and for recording wave patterns involving earthquake zones. It may also be valuable for air traffic control. D.A.T./G.B.

HOMEOSTASIS (hō′ mē ō stā′ səs) Homeostasis is the ability of a living thing to keep a steady, stable condition within its body. This internal environment is controlled by different body processes, such as respiration, circulation, and balance of body fluids. The nervous system and the hormones of the endocrine system play a major part in homeostasis. The excretion of wastes is an important part of homeostasis. In warm-blooded animals, excretion helps to maintain a constant body temperature.

Scientists believe that homeostasis shows the degree of evolution of a species. The steadier a living thing's internal systems are, the more independent it is of the external environment, and the more developed (advanced) it is.

The maintenance of social structures in populations of organisms is also regarded as homeostasis between organisms. *See also* ENVIRONMENT. J.J.A./E.R.L.

HOMOLOGUE (hō′ mə lóg′) In organic chemistry, certain compounds can be grouped together. These groups are called homologous series. A compound that belongs to such a group is called a homologue, or homolog. An example of a homologous series is the alkanes or paraffins. The first member is

Each chemical compound in a group is a homologue of others in the series.

Alkanes or paraffins	Primary alcohols	Olefins or alkenes	Aldehydes
methane CH_4	methyl alcohol CH_3OH		formaldehyde $HCHO$
ethane C_2H_6	ethyl alcohol C_2H_5OH	ethylene or ethene C_2H_4	acetaldehyde CH_3CHO
propane C_3H_8	propyl alcohol C_3H_7OH	propylene or propene C_3H_6	propionaldehyde C_2H_5CHO
n-butane C_4H_{10}	n-butyl alcohol C_4H_9OH	n-butylene or n-butene C_4H_8	n-butyraldehyde C_3H_7CHO

methane. Its chemical formula is CH_4. Next comes ethane (C_2H_6), then propane (C_3H_8), and so on. In this example, the formula for each homologue differs from the next by CH_2. This is true for all homologous series. Other homologous series include the alcohols, the aldehydes, and the alkenes, or olefins. Homologues have similar chemical properties and their physical properties change as you move through the series. For example, the melting and boiling points become higher. In the paraffins, the lowest members are gases. As you move through the series, they become liquids at normal temperatures, and then solids. M.E./J.M.

HONEY LOCUST (hən' ē lō' kəst) The honey locust is a tree that grows in the central United States. It grows to about 24 m [80 ft] tall. The leaves of the honey locust resemble a fern. Many—but not all—honey locust trees have thorns on their branches. The seeds of the tree are grown inside a dark brown pod that looks like a large string bean. The honey locust is common around lakes and streams. *See also* FERN. S.R.G./M.H.S.

HONEYSUCKLE FAMILY The honeysuckle (hən' ē sək' əl) family includes about 350 species of flowering dicotyledons. Most are shrubs or climbing plants native to temperate areas throughout the world. Two common shrubs in this family are the viburnum and the elder. (*See* ELDERBERRY.)

The honeysuckles belong to the genus *Lonicera.* Most are evergreens with opposite, dark green, oval leaves. The flowers are trumpet-shaped with four petals above and one petal below. The petals form a long tube which makes it difficult for most insects to pollinate them. Hawk moths and hummingbirds are the usual agents of pollination because they are able to reach into the base of the flower to get the nectar. The flowers give rise to red, orange, or black berries.

(*See* FRUIT.) These berries are a popular food of birds.

The common honeysuckle (*Lonicera periclymenum*) is a climbing plant that grows to a height of about 6 m [20 ft]. It has clusters of yellowish flowers with purple edges. The sweet honeysuckle (*Lonicera caprifolium*) has clustered, purplish white flowers which open at night and close during the day. *See also* ADAPTATION. A.J.C./M.H.S.

The common honeysuckle, *Lonicera periclymenum.*

HOOKE, ROBERT (1635–1703) Robert Hooke (hủk) was an English scientist. He made discoveries in many branches of physics and chemistry. He was also a clever designer. He helped Robert Boyle to design an air pump. His work was also useful in the designing of Newcomen's steam engine. In 1660, Hooke discovered that the strain on a material is proportional to the stress. This is called Hook's law. (*See* ELASTICITY.) The strain is the ratio of the amount it stretches to the

original length. The stress is the force per unit area applied. He made the first Gregorian telescope and also designed buildings.
C.M./D.G.F.

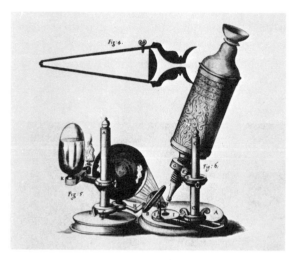

The microscope used by Robert Hooke in his studies of plant cells.

HOP (häp) Hop is one of four species of herbaceous plants belonging to the genus *Humulus*. Closely related to hemp, it also is classified in one of three families: mulberry family, nettle family, or the family Cannabaceae. (*See* CLASSIFICATION OF LIVING ORGANISMS.) Hops are native to temperate areas throughout the world.

The common hop (*Humulus lupulus*) is a tall, perennial, climbing plant with large, toothed leaves. It is a dioecious plant with either staminate (male) flowers in clusters or pistillate (female) flowers in a cone-shaped catkin. This catkin is covered with thin scales called bracts. The catkins are dried and used in brewing beer. *See also* HEMP. A.J.C./F.W.S.

HORIZON (hə rīz′ ən) The horizon is where the land or sea seems to meet the earth. It is also called the visible horizon. At sea, where there are no visual obstructions, the horizon appears about 4 km [2.5 mi] away.

The horizon appears farther away when viewed from a high place. This is because the earth is round. For example, an airplane pilot flying at a height of 1.6 km [1 mi] sees the horizon 158 km [98 mi] away. This is because the pilot is seeing farther over the curvature of the earth than a viewer at sea level.

The celestial horizon is the circle at which a plane, passing through the observer's location at a right angle to a point directly overhead, meets the celestial sphere. The celestial horizon is also called the astronomical horizon. *See also* CELESTIAL SPHERE; ZENITH.
J.M.C./C.R.

HORMONE

A hormone (hȯr′ mōn′) is a chemical substance that is produced in one part of an organism and has an effect on another part of that organism. Both plants and animals produce hormones. Hormones are vital body substances that act as "chemical messengers" to control body development and function. (*See* HOMEOSTASIS.)

Plant hormones Hormones are important in the growth and development of plants. Most plant hormones are concentrated in the growing regions such as the tips of stems and roots. The major plant hormones are auxins, cytokinins, and gibberellins. Auxins have several functions including causing the elongation of cells and the development of fruit. Auxins produced in the tip of the stem (the coleoptile) prevent side or lateral branches from growing. This is known as apical dominance. Auxins are also responsible for the tropisms. (*See* MOVEMENT OF PLANTS.) Cytokinins work closely with auxins by controlling cellular division and cellular differentiation. (*See* MITOSIS.) Gibberellins cause a plant to grow larger. All three of these hormones are closely related. Growth of a plant is controlled by the balance of these hormones.

Human hormones Most human hormones are produced by the endocrine or ductless glands. They are called ductless because they secrete hormones directly into the blood, and not into tubes or other structures. The blood carries the hormones throughout the body until they reach the ''target'' organ or tissue. Although the amount of each hormone in the blood is very tiny, it is tightly controlled within certain limits. Too much or too little of a hormone often has a harmful effect on the body. The major endocrine glands are the pituitary, the thyroid, four parathyroid glands, two adrenal glands, the islets of Langerhans, and the thymus gland.

The pituitary gland is located at the base of the brain. It is sometimes called the master gland because it secretes hormones which control most of the other glands. The pituitary itself is controlled by the hypothalamus, part of the brain. The pituitary has three sections: the anterior lobe, the intermediate lobe, and the posterior lobe. The anterior lobe produces six hormones. Adrenocorticotropic hormone (ACTH) controls the cortex of the adrenal glands. Thyroid stimulating hormone (TSH) controls the thyroid gland. Follicle stimulating hormone (FSH) and luteinizing hormone (LH) control the sex glands. Prolactin stimulates the production of milk in a mother who is breast-feeding her child. Growth hormone (GH) is sometimes called somatotropin. GH controls growth by controlling the way the body uses food in building tissues. Too much GH can cause a person to become a giant. Too little can cause a person to be a dwarf. If a large, abnormal amount of GH is produced in an adult, the result can be acromegaly.

The only hormone produced by the intermediate lobe is melanocyte stimulating hormone (MSH). In some vertebrates MSH controls pigment in the skin. The function of MSH in human beings, however, is unknown.

The posterior lobe produces two hormones. Vasopressin is also called antidiuretic hormone (ADH). ADH controls the amount of water present in the blood. Too little ADH can result in the disease diabetes insipidus. This disease is characterized by the loss of great amounts of water. It can lead to dehydration and death. Oxytocin causes the muscles of the uterus to contract when a pregnant woman begins labor. (*See* PREGNANCY.) It also helps cause the release of milk as a mother breast-feeds her baby. Recent experiments indicate that these two hormones are actually produced by the hypothalamus, and are simply stored in the posterior lobe of the pituitary.

The thyroid gland is located on both sides of the trachea in the throat. It produces two hormones which control body metabolism. Thyroxine and triiodothyronine regulate the rate at which cells use food to produce energy. Too much of these hormones can cause the condition known as exophthalmia, or bulging eyes. Over-production causes increased metabolism which results in nervousness, weight loss, weakness, and increased heartbeat. Too little of these hormones may cause the disease myxedema. This is characterized by decreased metabolism and results in sluggishness, weight gain, slow heartbeat, and general tiredness. In order for the thyroid gland to function properly, there must be enough iodine in the diet. Iodine is commonly added to table salt to prevent this deficiency. (*See* SODIUM CHLORIDE.) If there is a lack of iodine, goiter, or swelling of the thyroid gland, may result. If a pregnant woman has too little iodine in her diet, her child may be affected by cretinism. Cretinism results in mental and physical retardation.

The parathyroid glands are embedded in the thyroid gland. They produce parathyroid hormone or parathormone. This hormone controls the usage of calcium and phosphorous in the body. These minerals are vital for proper functioning of muscles, bones, and nerves. Too little parathormone can result in tetany, a general contracting of muscles which eventually can cause death. Too much parathormone can cause an excess of calcium in the blood. This results in kidney and bladder stones, kidney failure, increased blood pressure, and blood clots.

The adrenal glands are located on top of the kidneys. These glands have two sections: the outer adrenal cortex and the inner adrenal medulla. The adrenal cortex produces several hormones. Corticosterone and cortisol control the metabolism of carbohydrates, fats, and proteins. Aldosterone controls the salt balance in the body. (*See* SODIUM; POTASSIUM.) Androgen, like androsterone, is a male sex hormone. An injury or disease which affects the adrenal cortex may result in the underproduction of these hormones. This condition is called Addison's disease.

The adrenal medulla produces two hormones. Epinephrine and norepinephrine are also called adrenalin and noradrenalin. These hormones stimulate the nervous system in times of great stress. They increase the heart rate and the amount of energy available to the muscles.

The sex glands are the testes (testicles) and the ovaries. The testes produce testosterone, a male sex hormone. The ovaries produce three hormones. Estriol (an estrogen) and progesterone control the menstrual cycle. Progesterone is also important during pregnancy. Relaxin helps widen the birth canal (vagina) just before the birth of a baby.

The islets of Langerhans are part of the pancreas. They produce two hormones. Insulin decreases the amount of sugar in the blood. Too little insulin results in the disease diabetes mellitus. (*See* DIABETES.) Too much insulin can cause the disease hypoglycemia which is characterized by low blood sugar. Glucagon balances insulin, performing the opposite function. Glucagon releases sugar into the blood.

The thymus gland is located in the chest. It is large in infants and gets smaller as the child grows older. The thymus produces thymosin. Although its function is not clearly understood, thymosin apparently helps protect babies from disease. (*See* IMMUNITY.)

There are other hormones which are not produced by the endocrine glands. The hormones produced by the stomach, duodenum, and small intestines function in the digestion of food. They control the production of digestive juices.

Hormones in other animals Most mammals produce hormones similar to those of human beings. Other vertebrates and some invertebrates also produce hormones, though not as much is known about their functions. Pheromones are special hormones released into the environment by fish, insects, and other animals. Pheromones signal others of the same species and may be a mating signal or a warning of danger. The process of metamorphosis is also controlled by hormones.

How hormones work Hormones are generally divided into two groups. The steroids, such as those produced by the sex glands and the adrenal cortex, are relatively simple chemicals. The rest of the hormones are polypeptides, and are similar to amino acids and proteins.

Hormones work by changing the chemical activities in a cell. It is thought that the steroids enter the cell and affect the genes directly. Polypeptide hormones, however, stay outside the cell and attach to the cell membrane. This affects the enzymes, causing the production of a substance called cyclic AMP inside the cell. Cyclic AMP then causes chemical changes in the cell.

Uses of hormones Realizing the importance of hormones, scientists have tried to develop synthetic substitutes for the hormones. These can be used to treat hormonal deficiencies which may have been caused by malfunction, injury, or disease of one of the endocrine glands. In addition, hormones have been shown effective in treating other diseases. For example, cortisone is often used as a treatment for arthritis and allergies. Synthetic sex hormones are used in birth control pills. Birth control pills prevent a woman from producing an egg, and thus prevent her from becoming pregnant. (*See* CONTRACEPTION.) Synthetic plant hormones have been used for many years to increase crop production. Other hormones are fed to livestock to make them grow more quickly and produce more meat.   A.J.C./J.J.F.

HORNBEAM (hȯrn′ bēm′) The hornbeam is a small tree that grows in the central and eastern United States. It rarely exceeds 12 m [40 ft] in height. There are two well-known species of hornbeam: the American hornbeam and the eastern hop hornbeam. Both have very tough wood which is often used for handles of tools. The seeds are eaten by many songbirds and other wildlife. The trunk of the American hornbeam is very smooth with wide ridges.   S.R.G./M.H.S.

HORNBILL (hȯrn′ bil′) The hornbills are 45 species of tropical African and Asian birds that belong to the family Bucerotidae. They have huge bills which are usually filled with air spaces and covered with a thin layer of hard, bonelike material. These air spaces keep the bill lightweight. Hornbills have large heads and wings and long tails. They range in size from 38 to 150 cm [15 to 60 in] in length. Their feathers are usually brown or black with white markings. Most hornbills live in the tops of trees and eat fruits and insects.

In most species, a female lays her eggs in a hollow tree. The male then fills up the opening in the tree with clay and mud, locking the female and her eggs inside. A small hole is left so that the male can feed the female while she stays with the eggs. After the eggs have hatched, the male helps the female break out of her "prison." They may then fill in the opening again, leaving the baby hornbills inside. The adults feed the babies through a small hole until the babies are almost fully grown. The young hornbills are then freed. *See also* BIRD; TOUCAN.   A.J.C./L.L.S.

HORNBLENDE (hȯrn′ blend′) Hornblende is a shiny green, brown, or black mineral. It often occurs in the form of dark, needlelike crystals. Hornblende is a common mineral in igneous and metamorphic rocks. Some metamorphic rocks are composed entirely of hornblende. The chemical composition of hornblende is quite variable. It is a silicate and contains aluminum and other elements, such as sodium, potassium, iron, and magnesium. *See also* SILICA.   J.J.A./R.H.

HORNET (hȯr′ nət) Hornet is the name given to several species of large wasps. They are social insects that live in papery nests made from plant fibers which have been chewed and formed into a papier-mâché-like substance. A hornet colony consists of one or more queens (fertile females), many workers (sterile females), and, at times, several males. A queen starts the colony by building a small nest in which she lays only a few eggs. The unfertilized eggs develop into larvae which mature into workers. (*See* PARTHENOGENESIS.) The workers then increase the size of the nest, feed the queen and any developing larvae, and protect the nest. The queen now only lays eggs. By the end of the summer, a single nest may have thousands of worker hornets.

With colder weather, the queen leaves the nest to hibernate in a protected place. (*See* HIBERNATION.) All of the other hornets die, and the nest is abandoned. Next spring, the process is repeated as the queen comes out of hibernation and starts another nest. Hornets rarely use the same nest twice.

Two common hornets are the white-faced hornet (*Vespula maculata*) and the giant hornet (*Vespa crabro*). The giant hornet is also called the yellow jacket. Hornets are aggressive and dangerous insects. They sting by inserting the stinger and then injecting a poison. This poison causes swelling and intense pain. Hornet larvae, however, are helpful creatures as they feed on flies, caterpillars, and other harmful insects. *See also* WASP.

A.J.C./J.E.R.

HORSE (hȯrs) The horse (*Equus caballus*) is an ungulate, or hoofed mammal, belonging to the order Perissodactyla. It evolved from a small animal called eohippus that lived in North America and Europe more than 50 million years ago. (*See* EVOLUTION.)

Horses range in size from the largest, the draft horses, at 1,100 kg [2,420 lb] to the smallest, the Shetland ponies, at 140 kg [308 lb]. The height of a horse is measured in hands from the ground to the withers, a point between the shoulder blades on the back of the horse. A hand is the average width of a man's hand, or 10 cm [4 in]. The largest draft horses grow to a height of 20 hands (200 cm [6 ft 8 in]). The average horse is about 15.2 hands (155 cm [5 ft 2 in]) tall. Any full-grown horse that is shorter than 14.2 hands (147 cm [4 ft 10 in]) tall is called a pony.

A horse's body is covered with hair that may be a solid or mixed color, or may be spotted or splotched. It has a long tail which is used to brush away insects. The horse has large, keen eyes which can move in opposite directions at the same time. Its ears can be moved to "catch" faint sounds. Most male horses (stallions) have 40 teeth, while most females (mares) have 36 teeth. The age and health of a horse can be determined by counting the number of teeth and examining their condition.

The legs of a horse are well-suited for running. (*See* ADAPTATION.) The front legs are thinner than the hind legs and can withstand the shock of absorbing the horse's weight. The hind legs are larger and more muscular to provide the strength needed for running and jumping. The foot of the horse is made of one toe with a strong, hard hoof. The rear of the foot has a tough, elastic pad which acts like a rubber heel in absorbing shocks.

The mare has a gestation period of about 11 months, after which she gives birth to one colt (baby horse). The colt is able to walk and run a few hours after birth. It is full-grown by the time it is five years old. Stallions usually start mating when they are two years old, mares when they are three or four. Most mares will bear six colts during their lifetime, but some may bear as many as 19. Horses usually live for about 30 years.

Horses are herbivores and eat grass by biting it off near the ground. Horses have been

---

The modern horse, below, differs greatly from its ancestors, two of which are shown at the right. Note the difference in foot structure.

Eohippus lived in the Eocene epoch, about 50 million years ago.

Merychippus lived in the Miocene epoch, about 20 million years ago.

domesticated for thousands of years, and have been used for many purposes. The only truly wild horse still in existance is Przewalski's horse, a stocky, light brown animal living in small numbers on the plains of central Asia. The other so-called wild horses of today are actually domestic horses which escaped and started to live in the wild again. The number of these "wild horses," or mustangs, in the United States has dropped from several million in the 1800s to fewer than 20,000 today. For this reason, federal laws were established in 1971 to protect them from hunters.

A.J.C./J.J.M.

HORSE CHESTNUT (hòrs ches′ net) The horse chestnut is a tree that originally came from Asia and is now found throughout the United States. It is planted as an ornamental tree because it provides good shade and has a very lovely flower. The flowers are pink or white. They grow in conical clusters. Large nuts grow inside a green, spiny case. The tree is called a chestnut because the nut of the tree resembles the nut of the American chestnut. However, the two trees are not closely related. The horse chestnut tree grows to 24 m [80 ft] in height. *See also* CHESTNUT.

S.R.G./M.H.S.

HORSEFLY (hòrs′ flī′) The horsefly is any of several species of stout-bodied flies with

Front view of the head of a horsefly, showing its mouth parts and the brilliantly-colored eyes.

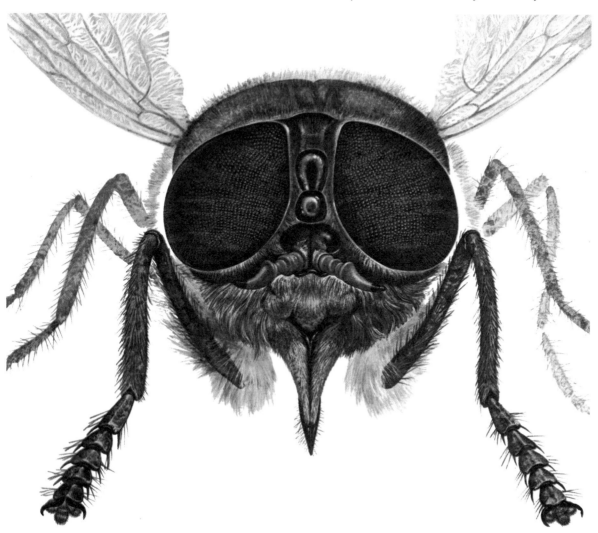

large, brilliantly colored compound eyes. (*See* EYE AND VISION.) The female bites human beings, horses, and other animals. After making the bite with the sharp mouthparts, she inserts a tubelike proboscis through which she sucks blood. Male horseflies usually feed on nectar and do not bite animals. Larvae develop from eggs which are usually laid near brooks or streams. The larvae eat earthworms and other small, soft animals.

The most common horsefly (*Tabanas atratus*) has a black body. Horseflies may carry disease-causing parasites and bacteria. The horsefly is sometimes called the gadfly. *See also* FLY. A.J.C./J.E.R.

HORSEHEAD NEBULA (hòrs′ hed neb′ yə lə) The Horsehead nebula is a dark cloud of gas and dust located in the constellation Orion. When viewed through a telescope, the Horsehead nebula has a greenish glow. The Horsehead nebula is so named because it resembles the shape of a horse's head. We can see this nebula because there is a bright nebula behind it, and the horsehead shape blocks the light from the bright nebula. *See also* NEBULA. J.M.C./C.R.

HORSEPOWER (hòr′ spaùr′) Horsepower is a unit of power used in the foot-pound-second system of units. (*See* FOOT-POUND-SECOND SYSTEM.) If you move a weight upwards, you are doing work against gravity. If you push a car along a level road, you are doing work against friction. Power is the rate at which work is done. Originally, one horsepower was reckoned to be the power of one horse. It was used to describe early steam engines. If a steam engine had a horsepower of two, then it could do the work of two horses. In the foot-pound-second system, one horsepower is equal to 550 foot-pounds per second. In the SI system of units, it is equal to 746 watts. (*See* INTERNATIONAL SYSTEM.)

For an automobile engine, the horsepower can be calculated from the rate of work of the pistons. This is called the indicated horsepower. Some of this power is used to overcome friction inside the engine. The rest of the indicated horsepower drives the automobile. This is called the brake horsepower. M.E./R.W.L.

HORSERADISH (hòrs′ rad′ ish) Horseradish (*Armoracia rusticana*) is a perennial, herbaceous plant belonging to the mustard family. It is native to Europe. It has long, toothed leaves growing from large roots. Clusters of small, white flowers grow along stems which are about 60 cm [2 ft] tall. The roots are grated for use in making the bitter, sharp-tasting relish which is also known as horseradish. *See also* MUSTARD FAMILY. A.J.C./F.W.S.

These horsetails grow in damp places in the northern temperate zones. They are living fossils.

HORSETAIL (hòr′ stāl′) The horsetail is any of 20 species of primitive land plants belonging to the genus *Equisetum*. Horsetails are distantly related to ferns and club mosses. They grow in damp places in temperate and tropical areas. They are usually small and treelike, except they have hollow stems. Horsetails grow from perennial rhizomes. (*See* RHIZOME.)

Horsetails do not produce flowers. Instead they produce reproductive stalks with cone-like structures containing spores. (*See* ASEXUAL REPRODUCTION.) Horsetails contain silica and were once used for polishing metal. This led to their nickname, scouring rush.

Horsetails are the sole survivors of an important group of plants of the Carboniferous period when some species grew as large as trees. Their remains form an important part of coal. A.J.C./M.H.S.

The horsetail has no roots. It grows from an underground rhizome. A vegetative shoot is at the right. The fertile stem at the left bears a "cone" containing spores.

HORTICULTURE (hòr' tə kəl' chər) Horticulture is a branch of agriculture that specializes in increasing the quality and quantity of fruits, vegetables, flowers, trees, and shrubs. Horticulturalists try to determine the best growing conditions for plants—including type of soil, types and amounts of fertilizers, methods of cultivation, and methods of insect, weed, and disease control.

Horticulture has led to the development of new, stronger, more productive varieties of plants. They have made it possible for farmers to produce more high quality food on less land. *See also* AGRICULTURE; BOTANY.

A.J.C./F.W.S.

HOUSEFLY (haùs' flī') The housefly (*Musca domestica*) is one of the most widely distributed of all insects. It is a major pest and health hazard, particularly in parts of the world where sanitary conditions are poor. The housefly has a dull gray, bristled body that is about 7 mm [0.3 in] long. It has large, reddish compound eyes. (*See* EYE AND VISION.) Its mouth cannot bite, but consists of a spongy pad. The housefly eats by oozing saliva and digestive juices over food and then sponging up the resulting solution. In this way, houseflies contaminate large amounts of food. Houseflies often carry one or more disease-causing microorganisms in their saliva or on their bodies and legs.

Houseflies usually live and breed in or near garbage or organic wastes (such as feces). The female lays about 100 eggs at a time and as many as 1,000 during her lifetime. The eggs hatch into larvae, or maggots, in 12 to 30 hours. The maggots molt several times before becoming pupae. (*See* MOLTING.) Within a few days, the pupae become adults and the cycle begins again. (*See* METAMORPHOSIS.) Most adult houseflies live for about 30 days in the summer, longer when the weather is cooler. Cold weather usually

A housefly feeding on meat is shown above. The fly pours saliva and other digestive juices on the meat and mops up the mixture with its spongy mouth—spreading germs as it does so.

kills off the adults, but larvae and pupae are able to survive the winter. *See also* FLY.

A.J.C./J.E.R.

HOVERCRAFT *See* AIR-CUSHION VEHICLE.

HOWLER MONKEY (haủ′ lər məng′ kē) The howler monkey is any of five species of monkeys belonging to genus *Alouatta* of the family Cebidae. They are the largest in this family, often growing to a height of 60 cm [2 ft] with tails at least that long. They weigh about 8 kg [17.6 lb] and have red, black, or brown fur. Howler monkeys live in tropical forests in South America.

The howler monkey gets its name from its deafening, howling roar. Its howl is so loud that it can be heard more than 3 km [1.8 mi] away. The sounds are made by a large, bony resonating chamber in the throat. This chamber produces an obvious swelling under the chin. Howler monkeys howl when they wake up in the morning and when disturbed

The howler monkey gets its name from its unpleasantly loud voice.

by noise or approaching rain. They also howl to warn off intruders in their territory. Howler monkeys live in trees, sometimes hanging by their tails while feeding on leaves and fruits. (*See* HERBIVORE.) These mammals usually travel in groups of 15 to 20. *See also* MONKEY; RESONANCE.

A.J.C./J.J.M.

HOYLE, SIR FRED (1915–   ) Sir Fred Hoyle (hòil) is a British astronomer. He is famous for his work on the origin of the universe. Hoyle suggested that new matter is being made in the universe all the time. But this idea is not now generally accepted. Hoyle has found that heavy elements can be formed inside stars. Stars change their nature as they get older. Hoyle has studied the way they change.

Hoyle has other interesting theories about physics. He has suggested that gravity might not always stay the same. This means that things could change in weight after a long time. His study of quasars had made him believe that our knowledge of physics is not great enough to understand them. He is also famous for his science-fiction stories. (*See* QUASARS.)

C.M./D.G.F.

HUBBLE, EDWIN POWELL (1889–1953) Edwin Hubble (həb′ əl) was a famous American astronomer. He was interested in nebulae and galaxies.

He worked at the Mount Wilson Observatory, with its famous 100-inch telescope (the largest in the world at that time). He used this telescope to find stars outside our own galaxy and to help show that there are other galaxies outside our own. In 1929, he showed that a characteristic of the light received from these galaxies could mean that the universe is expanding. (*See* RED SHIFT.)

Some scientists believe that all the matter of the stars was once concentrated in one very dense lump. The lump exploded, and the fragments became the stars. The stars are moving apart like bits of an exploding bomb.

Hubble calculated how long ago this explosion was. He believed it was about 10 billion years ago. The ratio of the speed at which the galaxies are moving to their distance from earth is called the Hubble constant. *See also* COSMOLOGY. C.M./D.G.F.

HUMAN BEING

Human beings (hyü′ mən bē′ ings) are unique among the creatures that inhabit the earth. Their cultures develop art, philosophy, technology, and religion. Highly developed language systems allow humans to communicate on complex levels.

The brain of human beings is highly developed. This results in the ability to think, work out problems, and form ideas. A combination of this unique brain and a highly developed voice enables human beings to speak. They therefore communicate their ideas to others. The skill with which human beings can use their hands is also unique. Using this skill, they can use tools, write, and create art—again allowing them to communicate ideas and to record them. All art, religion, science, literature, civilization, and culture are the results of such abilities.

Human beings are the only creatures to study themselves and their achievements. Anatomy studies the structure of the human body. Physiology is the study of how the body works. Through psychology, the human mind is explored. Sociology is the study of how people behave in groups. Anthropology includes the study of the differences between the various human races and cultures. Human beings study the nature and workings of the world around them through many branches of science, such as astronomy, biology, chemistry, geology, and physics. These studies, and many more, help people to understand themselves, to conquer diseases, and to plan for the future. Such studies have enabled people to survive in various surroundings. By developing agriculture, engineering, and medicine, people have been able to use and control many aspects of the environment to their advantage. Yet human beings are also the most destructive of creatures. Besides the capacity to destroy themselves and all other life, they have the ability to change the balance of nature. They create pollution and misuse pesticides that kill wildlife.

Scientific classification Within the animal kingdom, scientists place human beings in the subkingdom Metazoa. Metazoa includes all living things made up of many cells and having true digestive cavities. Human beings belong to the phylum Chordata. Chordata includes all creatures with a nerve cord and a notochord along the back. The human backbone puts human beings in the subphylum Vertebrata. Vertebrates form several classes, among them Mammalia, to which the human being belongs. Nearly all mammals give birth to live young and nurse them.

The more than 4,000 species of mammals make up 19 orders. Scientists place human beings, apes, monkeys, lemurs, and tarsiers in the order Primates. Primates have well-developed control over their fingers and toes, and can grasp objects easily. Most primates have excellent eyesight and stereoscopic vision. Stereoscopic vision allows them to judge depth. Human beings, monkeys, and apes make up the suborder Anthropoidea. People and apes alone form the superfamily Hominoidea. The family of human beings, the Hominidae, includes human beings of prehistoric times as well as all modern human races. Some scientists divide this family into two groups, genus *Australopithecus* and genus *Homo*. Other scientists divide the family Hominidae into several different species. Scientists agree that all living human beings today are genus *Homo,* species *sapiens.* *Homo sapiens* are latin words that mean "wise man."

The development of the human being Human beings and the apes have developed from the same primate ancestor. This ancestor is now extinct. The most important differences between apes and human beings are brain size and the ability to walk upright. *Ramepithecus,* an ape that lived about 12 million years ago, showed some human characteristics. However, true humanlike fossils do not occur until much later. Until recently the oldest humanlike fossil known was *Australopithecus.* But in 1972, Dr. Richard Leakey discovered a fossil skull in Kenya. This skull had a much larger brain then *Australopithecus.* This fossil is about 2.5 million years old. It could possibly represent the "missing link" between apes and human beings.

More recent fossils, dating from about 750,000 years ago, show definite relationships to human beings. *Pithecanthropus* was very humanlike. But *Pithecanthropus* had prominent ridges over the eyes and some apelike features. Other remains dating from that time are generally classified under *Homo erectus.* Examples are the Java man and Peking man. All fossils of *Homo erectus* are at least 400,000 years old. From this creature, several types of the human beings seem to have developed. One was the Neanderthal. The Neanderthal looked very primitive with thick, stocky body and enlarged eyebrow ridges. However, the Neanderthal possessed a large brain. The Neanderthals also used various stone tools and buried their dead. They lived in Europe until about 35,000 years ago, when human beings like ourselves replaced them.

The change came too quickly for the modern human being to have descended from the Neanderthals. The modern human being probably evolved separately, directly from *Homo erectus.* Some of the earliest known remains of *Homo sapiens,* such as the Steinheim man and the Swanscombe man, are 275,000 years old. Among the most famous prehistoric humans are those found in France at Cro-Magnon and elsewhere. They lived in caves. The caves were decorated with drawings.

Races of human beings All modern human beings are placed in the same biological species, *Homo sapiens.* Many people have suggested that human beings be divided into five main races. They are Caucasoid, meaning "white skinned," Negroid, meaning "black skinned," Mongoloid, meaning "yellow skinned," Australoid (the Australian aborigines), and Capoid (the Bushmen of South Africa). Other anthropologists, people who study human groups, reject racial classifications. But anthropologists nevertheless study the relationships among groups living in various parts of the world (*See* ANTHROPOLOGY.)

Because of all their mental and physical abilities, human beings have come to dominate most other living things. They have adapted themselves to their surroundings. They have also adapted nature to their needs. People have built machines that carry them around the world. They have built cities that hold millions of people. They have split atoms, shot rockets into space, and spun satellites around the earth.

Although human beings may harness nature, they are not free from the laws that govern all living things. People have slowly come to realize that they must work to conserve the earth's natural resources. Only in this way will future generations be able to carry on the way of life that they have created.

For thousands of years, human beings have searched for spiritual essences, or values that give meaning to life. Their sense of beauty is communicated in works of art. This creates an international language. Philosophy shows the human need for truth. Indeed, it is this unique quality of imagination, of thinking beyond the world around him, that has placed human beings, for better or worse, where they are.   J.J.A./J.J.M.

HUMBOLDT, BARON ALEXANDER VON (1769–1859)

Baron Alexander von Humboldt (hùm′ bōlt) was a German scientist and explorer. He is famous for his travels in South America, Europe, and Asia. He used the information that he collected on his travels to add to knowledge in many fields. Humboldt drew the first isothermal map. This showed the different climates of different places. He also linked this information with the types of plants that grew in different places. He studied volcanoes and sea currents. The cold current that flows north from the West coast of South America is named after him.

Humboldt turned his five-year journey around South America (1799–1804) into a book. The book took 20 years to write. It was full of new information about biology, astronomy, and geology. His last book was called *Kosmos*. In this book, Humboldt tried to show the way everything in the universe fits together.   C.M./D.G.F.

HUMERUS

(hyüm′ rəs) The humerus is a large bone in the upper half of the arm. The humerus lies between the shoulder and the elbow. The upper part of the bone has a ball-shaped head. This head fits into a cup-shaped hollow or socket in a large bone in the back called the shoulder blade.

The head of the humerus can move around quite freely in its socket. This allows the arm to move in many directions.   J.A./J.J.F.

HUMIDITY

(hyü mid′ ət ē) Humidity is the amount of water vapor in the air. It is always changing, because the warmer the air is, the more water vapor it can hold. Absolute humidity measures the amount of water vapor in a given volume of air.

At any given temperature, the air can only hold a certain amount of water vapor. If the air is holding as much water vapor as it possibly can, the air is said to be saturated. When this happens, the temperature is equal to the dew point, and some of the water vapor condenses out of the air in the form of dew or fog. (*See* CONDENSATION.)

Relative humidity is the amount of water vapor in the air compared to the amount needed for saturation. When the air is saturated, the relative humidity equals 100%. If the air is holding half as much water vapor as it possibly can, the relative humidity equals 50%.

Meteorologists measure relative humidity with an instrument called a hygrometer. Humidity has a significant effect on comfort, especially on hot days. On a hot day with high humidity, most people feel sticky because perspiration does not evaporate off their bodies. (*See* EVAPORATION.) The very low humidity associated with bitter cold winter weather gives people a biting sensation in the winter air. *See also* METEOROLOGY.

J.M.C./C.R.

HUMMINGBIRD

(həm′ ing′ bərd) A hummingbird is a very small bird that belongs to the family Trochilidae. There are 15 species found in North America. Fourteen species are found only in the western and southwestern part of North America. Only the ruby-throated hummingbird is found east of the Mississippi River. Hummingbirds are the smallest of all North American birds. The smallest, the Calliope hummingbird, is only 7.5 cm [2.75 in] long. The largest, the blue-throated hummingbird, is 13.1 cm [5.25 in] long. Most species are about 6.8 cm [3 in] long. Hummingbirds are so named because

Hummingbirds feed mainly on nectar. They hover in front of blossoms and plunge their long beak into the nectar.

their wings beat so fast they make a humming sound. They can hover in midair and even fly backwards. Hummingbirds have a high metabolism. (*See* METABOLISM.) They require large amounts of food to survive. The birds eat sugar-rich nectar which they suck out of flowers with their long, slender bills and tongues. S.R.G./L.L.S.

HUMUS (hyü′ məs) Humus is the dark, rich part of soil. It comes from dead plants and animals. The plants and animals die, fall to the ground, and slowly rot and are mixed into

Humus is a valuable component of soil. Humus is formed from decayed plant and animal materials. Leaves add to humus.

the dirt. This process returns the nutrients back to the soil where they came from. (*See* NUTRITION.) A sandy beach has no humus. The soil in a forest has a lot of humus. The leaves from the trees that die and fall to the ground help to build up humus. Humus allows plants to grow better. S.R.G./R.J.B.

HURRICANE (hər′ ə kān′) A hurricane is a violent tropical cyclone, with winds of at least 119 km [74 mi] per hour. Tropical cyclones are named according to where they form. A hurricane forms in the western North Atlantic Ocean, a typhoon in the west Pacific, a cyclone in the Indian Ocean, and a willy-willy near Australia.

Hurricane formation There are several requirements for hurricane formation. They can only develop over ocean waters of at least 27°C [80°F]. The area of formation must be at least 5° latitude away from the equator. At the equator there is no Coriolis force. The Coriolis force is needed to produce cyclonic wind circulation. Cyclonic winds are counterclockwise in the northern hemisphere, clockwise in the southern hemisphere. If the first two requirements for creating a hurricane are met, a large mass of thunderstorms can combine to form a common updraft, thus creating an area of low atmospheric pressure. Winds begin to revolve in a cyclonic direction around the low pressure area. At the same time, water is being evaporated and condensed, pumping energy into the system.

There are three stages in the formation of a hurricane. Tropical depression is the stage where the storm is rather undefined but appears to be strengthening. When the depression gains more power, it is called a tropical storm. When the wind speed reaches 119 km [74 mi] per hour, it is called a hurricane.

Hurricane structure   The center of the hurricane is a calm area called the eye. This area of lowest atmospheric pressure measures about 5 to 15 km [3 to 5 mi] in diameter. In the eye, the weather is calm and the skies may be clear. Surrounding the eye is a doughnut-shaped area called the anulus. In the anulus exists the most violent weather of the hurricane. Huge cumulonimbus clouds form a wall around the eye. (*See* CLOUD.) Severe thunderstorms and winds of 209 to 241 km [130 to 150 mi] per hour have been recorded. Surrounding the anulus is a large spiral-shaped area of rain and scattered thunderstorms. The full diameter of a mature hurricane is usually from 480 to 960 km [300 to 600 mi], and sometimes larger. The clouds may reach 5.5 km [18,000 ft] into the atmosphere.

Hurricane movement and destruction   Hurricanes usually move westward at first, but then shift to north or northeast. This movement makes the Gulf of Mexico coast and the eastern United States particularly vulnerable to a hurricane.

Hurricanes are usually preceded by a storm surge. Storm surges are great waves that may cause extensive damage to coastal areas. As the hurricane moves over land, strong winds and rain increase in intensity until the eye arrives. There may be an hour of calm winds and no precipitation. But when the eye moves on, the full fury of the storm returns.

Hurricanes rapidly lose energy after they reach land. This happens because the moisture source is cut off, and because of friction between the storm and the land. If a hurricane gets far enough north, it may cross a front, and be transformed into a regular storm.

The National Weather Service watches all hurricane activity, and informs the public of any important developments. If a hurricane threatens a land area, a hurricane warning is issued. This means that the population of that area must take the necessary precautions to avoid damage and casualties. *See also* METEOROLOGY.   J.M.C./C.R.

Hurricane Gladys was photographed from the United States Apollo 7 spacecraft in 1968.

HUTTON, JAMES (1726–1797) James Hutton (hət′ ən) was a Scottish geologist. He began by studying medicine, then became a farmer. Through farming and studying chemistry, he became interested in geology. This was not a real science when Hutton started work. His most important idea was that geological changes are continuously going on. Until then, scientists had believed that the earth changed in sudden bursts, which they called catastrophes.   C.M./D.G.F.

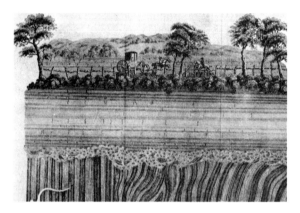

Illustration in James Hutton's *Theory of the Earth.*

HUYGENS, CHRISTIAN (1629–1695) Christian Huygens (hȯi′ gəns) was a Dutch scientist. He studied mathematics, physics, and astronomy. He was interested in light and made what was then the biggest telescope in the world. He found one of the moons of Saturn with this telescope, and saw the planet's rings. He invented the first pendulum clock in 1657. Huygens' most famous work is the discovery of polarized light. He also developed the wave theory of light. *See also* LIGHT; POLARIZED LIGHT.   C.M./D.G.F.

HUYGENS' PRINCIPLE (hȯi′ gəns prin′ spəl) Huygens' principle helps us understand how waves behave. It was first proposed by Christian Huygens, a Dutch scientist. It states that each point in a wave can be thought of as the source of more waves. For example, suppose that sound is entering a room through an open door. Huygens' principle says that, in

effect, the doorway is the source of the sound. The waves reaching you behave as if this were so.

Huygens' principle is very useful in the study of light. It is used to work out problems in diffraction and interference. (*See* DIFFRACTION; INTERFERENCE.) For example, if light passes through a narrow slit, the light is diffracted. This causes it to spread out. The slit can be regarded as the source of light. This allows the spreading of the light to be more easily understood.   M.E./S.S.B.

HYACINTH (hī′ ə sinth) The hyacinth is a spring flower of the lily family Liliaceae. Its bell-shaped flowers of blue, pink, white, yellow, or purple, bloom in March and April on stalks that grow from 15 to 46 cm [6 to 18 in] high. Hyacinths grow from bulbs in open beds, hothouses, and in the home.

The hyacinth originated in Asia and Africa, and was brought to Europe in the early 1500s. Today, it is a popular plant in many parts of the world. The soil and climate of the Netherlands provide a particularly favorable place for growing hyacinths. The Dutch plant a large number every year near Haarlem, Holland. They ship the bulbs to many parts of the world, including the United States.

Hyacinths raised in open beds need rich, well-drained soil. The bulbs are planted between September and November, and flowers appear in the early spring. Gardeners usually tie the stems to stakes for added support. In summer the bulbs are dug and stored after the leaves have withered.   W.R.P./M.H.S.

HYATT, JOHN WESLEY (1837–1920) John Hyatt (hī′ ət) was an American printer who invented many different things. He worked out a way of purifying a large amount of water. He also invented a roller bearing that is still used in modern machinery. His most interesting work was in the use of cellulose. He read that a prize was to be given for the best idea for making a synthetic billiard ball. Billiard balls then were made of ivory, which was very rare and expensive. Hyatt made a mixture of nitrocellulose, camphor, and alcohol. This could be molded under pressure when it was gently warmed. He won the prize and patented his invention in 1870. He also worked out a way of making thin sheets of celluloid good enough to use for photography. Hyatt's work with cellulose made him one of the pioneers of the plastics industry. *See also* PLASTIC; PHOTOGRAPHY.

C.M./D.G.F.

HYBRID (hī' brəd) A hybrid is the offspring of two parents that belong to different species, stock, breeds, or races. The mule is an example of a hybrid animal. Its parents are a jackass (male donkey) and a mare (female horse). The parents of some hybrids differ only slightly. Hybrid plants, such as corn, are produced by plants that differ in only a few traits. If the parents of a hybrid are very different, the hybrid may be sterile (unable to reproduce). The mule is one of those kinds of hybrids.

Hybrids occur naturally, and some are created by man's actions. Sometimes, in the case of natural hybrids, new species are created that are better able to handle their surroundings than their parents. Each parent of a hybrid has a different set of genes, and these genes are passed on to the offspring during reproduction. Some hybrids, particularly dogs, are called mongrels.

New plants can be developed through hybridization. The best hybrids may be superior to the parents in hardiness, yield, and resistance to disease. The cultivated strawberry is a good example. It has larger fruit and better flavor than its wild parents. Some hybrid tomatoes contain more vitamins than either parent. Hybrid corn produces higher yields, and withstands disease and drought better than regular varieties.

Hybridization in plants was developed in the early 1900s when scientists developed breeding methods based on Gregor Mendel's theories of plant heredity.

Hybridization in animals is more difficult than hybridization in plants. Plant crosses are easier to control than animal crosses. The cattalo is an example of a successful hybrid animal. The cattalo is a cross between domestic cattle and the American buffalo. Cattle breeders have also successfully crossed Brahman cattle of India with Afrikanders cattle of Africa. This hybrid endures the heat and humidity of the tropics, and resists diseases better than its parents and other varieties. Hybrid fowl, like chicken and turkeys, have been developed to produce more white meat on their breasts.

Animal hybridization is limited. Many animals are unable to mate because their genes do not react correctly. *See also* BURBANK, LUTHER; MENDEL, GREGOR.

W.R.P./M.H.S.

HYDRA (hī' drə) The hydra is one of the simplest multicellular animals and is one of the very few members of the phylum Cnidaria that lives in fresh water. (*See* CNIDARIA.) The largest hydras are only about 15 mm [0.6 in] long. The body of the hydra is called a polyp. Polyps are tube-shaped and sessile, meaning they usually stay in one place. The hydra attaches to underwater plants by means of a tiny pedal disk. It sometimes moves by sliding along on this pedal disk or by somersaulting through the water.

The hydra has a mouth opening at the unattached end of its body. The mouth is surrounded by five or six tentacles which are used to capture insect larvae and tiny water animals. Prey are paralyzed by a poison injected through nematocysts, tiny stinging threads in the tentacles. The hydra is said to have an incomplete digestive system because food enters and wastes leave through the same opening.

Hydras usually reproduce by budding,

each bud becoming a new organism. (*See* ASEXUAL REPRODUCTION; BUDDING.) In cool weather, however, hydras reproduce sexually. The hydra forms sperms and eggs which join within its body to form embryos. (*See* HERMAPHRODITE.) These embryos develop tough coats which protect them from drying or temperature changes. This is probably an adaptation to allow hydras to survive in areas where their habitat (ponds or lakes) dry up for part of the year.

Hydras can regenerate lost parts and, in fact, regenerate all their body cells every few weeks. (*See* REGENERATION.)

The most common hydras are the green hydra (*Chlorohydra viridissima*) and the brown hydra (*Pelmatohydra oligactis*). They get their color from algae which live symbiotically within the inner layer of cells of the hydras. (*See* SYMBIOSIS.)   A.J.C./C.S.H.

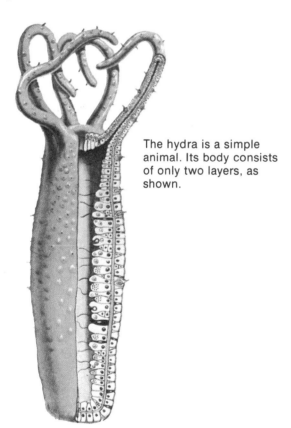

The hydra is a simple animal. Its body consists of only two layers, as shown.

HYDRANGEA (hī drān′ jə) The hydrangea is a genus of handsome, flowering shrubs in the Saxifragaceae family. One species grows 9 m [30 ft] high. A dwarf variety grows to about 3.7 m [12 ft]. The flowers are white, pink, or bluish, and grow in large, showy clusters. Each individual flower has 4 or 5 petals. Hydrangeas grow best in rich, slightly moist soil and in partially shaded areas. They bloom from late summer until fall. Hydrangeas are found in North and South America, China, and Japan.

Pink hydrangeas produce blue flowers when grown in soil treated with aluminum sulfate, or alum. Lime added to the soil makes blue hydrangeas produce pink flowers. Hydrangeas are grown by planting either cuttings or seeds.   W.R.P./M.H.S.

HYDRATE (hī′ drāt) A hydrate is a compound that forms crystals containing water. The water molecules are linked to the molecules of the compound. The water is called water of crystallization. The number of molecules of water can be shown in the chemical formula. For example, the formula for sodium carbonate is Na_2CO_3. When it forms a hydrate, it takes up ten molecules of water. The formula is now $Na_2CO_3 \cdot 10\ H_2O$.

The salts of some metals form more than one hydrate. Copper sulfate forms at least three. They can be written $CuSO_4 \cdot H_2O$, $CuSO_4 \cdot 3H_2O$, and $CuSO_4 \cdot 5H_2O$. Copper sulfate in the form of its hydrate makes deep blue crystals. If it is heated, the water of crystallization evaporates. The blue color disappears. White powder is left, containing no water. This is copper sulfate in its anhydrous state. Anhydrous means without water. When water is added, the blue color returns.

Some hydrates lose their water without heating. When the air is dry, their crystals become white and powdery. This is called efflorescence. Cobalt chloride shows a color change when it gains water. When it is a hydrate it forms pink crystals. It is blue when it is anhydrous. It can be used to show whether there is moisture inside a container or not. The blue crystals become pink if moisture is present. D.M.H.W./A.D.

HYDRAULICS (hī drȯ′ liks) Hydraulics is a branch of physics with several subdivisions. It is the study of the characteristics and behavior of fluids (or liquids) at rest and in motion. Practical uses of liquids include hydraulic engineering (control of rivers, irrigation systems, water supply systems) and mechanical engineering (machine design, such as water turbines, hydraulic jacks and presses, and pumps).

The basic difference between a liquid and a gas is that a liquid cannot be compressed. This characteristic of liquids makes them very useful for some kinds of work. The molecules of liquids can move about easily but cannot be squeezed any closer together. When pressure is applied to liquid in a sealed container, the liquid transfers the pressure equally in every direction. Pressure applied to fluid at one end of a fluid-filled tube is instantly transmitted to the other end.

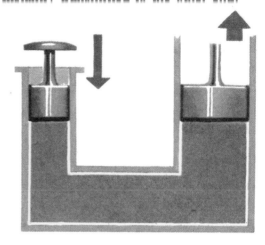

Above: Diagram of the principle of the hydraulic press. Pressure applied to the smaller piston is transferred instantly but with greater force to the larger piston. Below: Cut-away view of a hydraulic tractor hitch. The pressure of oil pumped through a pipe is transferred to the ram cylinder and applied against the larger area of the piston.

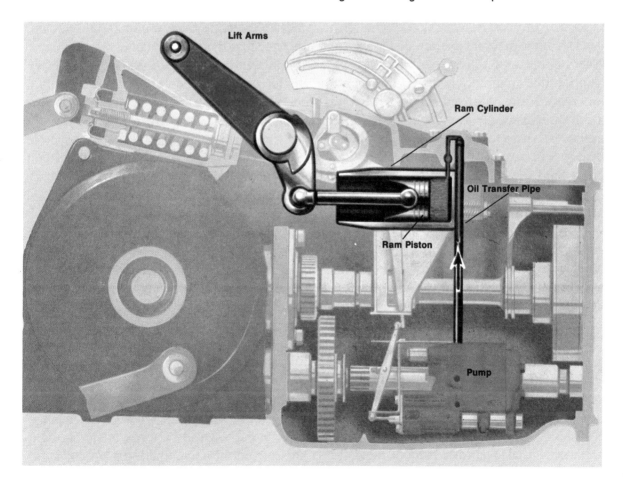

Lift Arms

Ram Cylinder

Oil Transfer Pipe

Ram Piston

Pump

The large earth scraper above uses a number of hydraulic mechanisms.

The study of liquids at rest (hydrostatics) considers such things as buoyancy and pressure. The behavior of liquids at rest is described by the laws of hydrostatics. One such law is that the pressure exerted by the weight of a column of fluid is determined by the height of the column. Another is that an object placed in a fluid will seem to lose as much weight as the weight of the fluid it displaces. These two laws explain why some objects will float while others will sink in a given fluid.

The study of liquids in motion (hydrokinetics) deals with such things as friction and velocity of water as it moves through pipes, valves, and nozzles. It deals also with hydraulic pressure in machines. One of the laws of hydrokinetics is that the velocity of a fluid moving through a pipe will decrease if the area of the pipe increases, and vice versa. The velocity of water moving under pressure through a garden hose is less than its velocity when moving through the smaller opening of the nozzle.

Hydraulic machines   Water and other liquids can be used to perform work by means of their motion or pressure. The waterwheel is a simple example of work performed by the motion of a liquid. The pressure can be simply that of the weight of the liquid, or it can be applied by an external force. Machines that make use of fluid motion or pressure are often called hydraulic engines or machines.

The turbine is an example of a rotary engine that uses a continuous stream of fluid to turn a shaft (usually at high speeds) to operate machines or perform other work. Water turbines are commonly used to operate electric generators. Water flowing over a dam provides a constant source of natural energy that can be used to turn a turbine engine. (*See* TURBINE.)

Water or other fluids placed under pressure can perform many kinds of work. Most hydraulic machines use a fluid that will not readily freeze, such as oil or silicone. Automobiles, tractors, bulldozers, dumptrucks, aircraft, industrial robots, car washes, and many other kinds of machines make use of hydraulic mechanisms.

In an automobile, foot-pressure on a pedal is transferred to a fluid and multiplied many times to operate the braking mechanism in each wheel. It takes relatively light pressure on the pedal to bring a moving automobile to a halt because of the law of hydraulic pressure. Pressure applied to a small piston by movement of the brake pedal is increased by being applied, via a tube filled with fluid, to a larger piston. If the diameter of the larger piston is five times that of the smaller piston, five times as much pressure is applied to the larger piston; and for every five inches the smaller piston moves, the larger piston will move one inch.

The use of pistons and valves in a hydraulic press or jack is the most common application of hydrokinetics. In some machines, the pressure is mechanically applied. In others, a reservoir of oil or other liquid is placed under pressure by a pump; and the pressure is applied to the desired piston by a system of valves. One of the advantages of a hydraulic mechanism is that it can be stopped and held at any point of travel.

Examples of mechanisms operated by a hydraulic press or jack are the flight-control surfaces of aircraft (ailerons, flaps, elevators, rudders, landing gear), barber's and dentist's chairs, and some automobile jacks. On a bulldozer or snowplow, a hydraulic mechanism positions the blade. Scrap-metal dealers use metal compactors operated by large, powerful hydraulic presses. *See also* BAROMETER; LIQUID; MOLECULE.   P.G.Z./G.D.B.

HYDRAZINE (hī′ drə zēn′) Hydrazine (N_2H_4) is a colorless liquid with an unpleasant odor resembling that of ammonia. Hydrazine boils at 113.5°C [236.3°F] and it freezes at 1.4°C [34.5°F]. It is a flammable liquid and is used as a fuel in rocket and jet engines. Hydrazine is sometimes added to water in boilers. It helps to prevent rust forming on the inside of the boiler.   M.E./J.M.

HYDRIDE (hī′ drīd) A hydride is a compound of an element with hydrogen. Hydrides may be made by directly combining the element with hydrogen gas. Sometimes a catalyst is needed to make the reaction work.

Hydrides may also be formed by using reducing agents. (*See* OXIDATION AND REDUCTION.) A reducing agent is a chemical compound that supplies atoms of hydrogen. When a compound accepts hydrogen in a reaction, it is said to be reduced.

There are several kinds of hydrides. Sodium, potassium, and lithium are elements high in the electromotive series. They combine with hydrogen to give sodium hydride, potassium hydride, and lithium hydride. These readily give up their hydrogen in chemical reactions. They are good reducing agents. Lithium aluminum hydride ($LiAlH_4$) is a particularly strong reducing agent.

Elements low in the electromotive series also combine with hydrogen. The halogens are examples. With chlorine, hydrogen forms hydrogen chloride. It could also be thought of as chlorine hydride. In the same way, bromine hydride is more usually called hydrogen bromide. These compounds dissolve in water to form strong acids.

Nonmetals such as nitrogen and phosphorus also combine with hydrogen. Again, the compounds are not normally called hydrides. With nitrogen, hydrogen forms ammonia (NH_3). With phosphorus it forms phosphine (PH_3). With carbon, hydrogen forms a huge number of different compounds. They are called the hydrocarbons.

Palladium forms hydrides with large quantities of hydrogen. This also happens with some other transition metals. These may not be true compounds, however. They may be mixtures of elements with hydrogen. They are rather like alloys.   D.M.H.W./A.D.

HYDROCARBONS (hī′ drə kär′ bənz) Hydrocarbons are important compounds of carbon and hydrogen. Because they contain carbon, they are organic compounds. They are found naturally in coal and oil and as gases under the earth. Gasoline, kerosene and candle wax all consist of hydrocarbons. Many hydrocarbons are valuable as fuels. There are two kinds of compounds that carbon and hydrogen can form. They are called the aliphatic compounds and the aromatic compounds.

Aliphatic hydrocarbons In aliphatic hydrocarbons, the carbon atoms are linked together in short or long chains or, sometimes, in rings. The chains may be straight or have branches to the sides. Carbon has a valence of four. This means that each atom can link with four other atoms. It is possible to make a huge molecule by linking carbon atom after carbon atom together. Hydrogen atoms are attached to the sides of the chain. Each hydrogen atom forms a link, or bond, with one carbon atom. A carbon atom may have a single bond with another carbon atom, or a double bond, or even a triple bond.

The simplest hydrocarbon of all is methane. This has one carbon surrounded by four atoms of hydrogen. Its formula is CH_4. Methane is marsh gas. It is found in natural gases. Ethane is another gas. It has two carbon atoms joined together by a single bond. All the other bonds are with hydrogen atoms. The formula for ethane is C_2H_6. Propane is C_3H_8, and butane is C_4H_{10}. Octane has eight carbon atoms linked together. Its formula is C_8H_{18}. Octane is important in gasoline. This series of compounds is called the alkane, or paraffin, series.

The series of compounds that has two carbon atoms joined by double bonds is called the alkene or olefin series. (*See* OLEFIN.) The simplest alkene is ethylene. Its formula can be written $CH_2\!=\!CH_2$. Ethylene is used to make the plastic polyethylene by polymerization. Compounds with more than one double bond are called alkadienes or diolefins. An example is butadiene, $CH_2\!=\!CH\!-\!CH\!=\!CH_2$. Butadiene is used to make synthetic rubber. Alkynes have one triple bond. Acetylene is an example. Its formula is $CH\!\equiv\!CH$. The alkanes are all saturated compounds. This means that they have the maximum number of hydrogen atoms in each molecule. They have no double or triple bonds. The alkenes, diolefins and alkynes do not have the maximum number of hydrogen atoms in each molecule. They have double or triple bonds between carbon atoms. They are unsaturated.

Cyclic aliphatic hydrocarbons Some aliphatic compounds consist of carbon atoms arranged in rings. If the rings consist only of carbon atoms, they are called alicyclic compounds. Cyclohexane (C_6H_{12}) is an example. It has six -CH_2- groups joined together by single bonds. Compounds containing rings of carbon atoms with one or more other kinds of atoms joined into the ring are called heterocyclic compounds.

Aromatic hydrocarbons Aromatic hydrocarbons have a special ring structure. They are called aromatic because they have a strong smell. Aromatics are based on the structure of benzene (C_6H_6). A molecule of benzene consists of six carbon atoms forming a ring. The bonds between these atoms continually alternate between single and double. This is the chemical phenomenon known as resonance. Naphthalene consists of two benzene rings linked together.

Substituted hydrocarbons Both aliphatic and aromatic hydrocarbons form more complicated compounds. This happens when hydrogen atoms in the hydrocarbons are replaced by other atoms or, in some cases, by chains of atoms. For example, chloroform, the anesthetic, consists of methane in which three of the hydrogen atoms have been replaced by chlorine atoms—$CHCl_3$. Aromatic hydrocarbons also form substituted compounds in the same way. For example, phenol (C_6H_5OH) consists of a benzene ring in which one hydrogen atom has been replaced by an -OH group. Sometimes an aromatic compound has an aliphatic chain attached to it.

M.E./A.I.

HYDROCHLORIC ACID (hī′ drə klōr′ ik as′ əd) Hydrochloric acid is a strong acid. It is made by dissolving hydrogen chloride gas in water. Its formula is HCl. Concentrated hydrochloric acid contains 39% hydrogen chloride. It is a colorless liquid when it is absolutely pure. It usually has a yellowish color when there are impurities. The acid is very poisonous and dangerous. It is extremely corrosive. It burns holes in clothes and eats into metal. It gives off fumes in moist air. It must be handled very carefully.

When hydrochloric acid reacts with many metals, bubbles are given off. Hydrogen gas is produced. At the same time the salt of the acid is formed. The salts of hydrochloric acid are called chlorides. Chlorides are also formed when hydrochloric acid reacts with bases.

Hydrochloric acid can be manufactured by bubbling hydrogen chloride gas through water. Another method is to add concentrated sulfuric acid to sodium chloride (common salt). Chlorine gas also produces hydrochloric acid when it reacts with certain hydrocarbons.

Hydrochloric acid is used to produce other chemicals. It is used to make dyes and to produce textiles and leather goods. It is also used in the manufacture of glues and glucose. In many industries it is used to clean metal surfaces. In the automobile industry it is used to remove rust and dirt before automobile parts are plated or painted. This is called pickling the metal.

Hydrochlorides are also salts of hydrochloric acid. They are formed when the acid reacts with an organic base. Many drugs and medicines are hydrochlorides. *See also* ACID; BASE; CHLORIDE; HYDROCARBON.

D.M.H.W./A.D.

HYDROELECTRIC POWER (hī′ drō i lek′ trik paùr′) Hydroelectric power is power that is obtained from the energy of flowing water. If we want to, we could produce power from even little streams. Moving water can be made to turn wheels. The wheels can be made to turn electrical generators. The electricity would cost very little to produce. The country needs a vast electricity supply. So we usually harness the biggest rivers possible.

The most power comes from water that is falling a great distance. Water that is high up has high potential energy. We can tap this energy only when the water falls to a lower level. The name for the distance that the water falls is the head. The head of water in a slow-moving river may be only a few inches in many miles. This would not supply much power. The head of water in a waterfall may be thousands of times greater. Waterfalls are an excellent source of hydroelectric power. Unfortunately there are not enough natural waterfalls to meet our needs. We have to make our own.

By damming a stream or river, we can create artificial falls. The water builds up behind a dam, and the head increases. A dam built across a valley gives a head of water equal to the height of the dam. Hydroelectric schemes are often graded by their heads. A low scheme has a head under 31 m [100 ft]. A medium one has a head of 31 to 155 m [100 to 500 ft]. A high one is anything over 155 m [500 ft]. High schemes usually have sites up in mountainous areas. Here it is possible to dam whole valleys. Valuable land is not lost when the valley becomes flooded. Low-site schemes are usually at the outlets of rivers. They are sometimes called run-of-the-river schemes. The dam, or barrage, simply directs the river water so that if flows through turbines.

The powerhouse of a hydroelectric scheme is often built at the foot of the dam. Inside are the turbines. They have blades which are forced around by the water as it flows. The power of the turbines is used to work the electrical generators. There are several different kinds of turbines.

Different kinds of turbines are suitable for different heads of water. For medium and

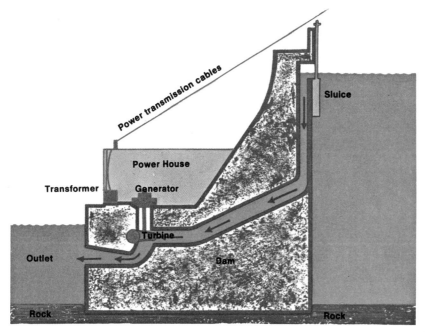

Left: diagram of a typical hydroelectric power station. When the sluice is lowered, the water behind the dam flows and turns the turbines, which turn the generators that make electricity. Transformers step up the electricty to very high voltage.

Below: three kinds of turbines used in hydroelectric systems. Pelton is an impulse type; Francis, a reaction type; Kaplan, a propeller type. Each is suited for different conditions.

high heads, impulse turbines are often used. For medium and low heads, reaction turbines are used. The number and type of turbines depend upon how much power is to be generated. By turning the generators, the turbines produce electricity. Near to the powerhouse is a transformer. This is used to adjust the voltage of the supply fed into the grid. (*See* ELECTRICITY SUPPLY.)

The pipelines that carry water to the turbines are called penstocks. They lead from behind the dam through to the powerhouse. The powerhouse is sometimes located at a distance from the dam. The lower down it is, the greater the head will be. If the powerhouse is a long way away, another system is used. Water from the dam is led into a small reservoir called a forebay. It passes through a tunnel or an aqueduct. Penstocks carry the water from the forebay down to the powerhouse.

A surge shaft is another important part of a hydroelectric scheme. It is a safety device. When the flow of water to a turbine is cut down, there is a sudden build-up of pressure. This is due to the inertia of the water in the penstock. It could burst through and damage the turbine. The surge shaft is a way of absorbing the shock. It is a vertical pipe joining

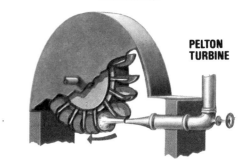

PELTON TURBINE

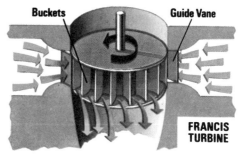

Buckets

Guide Vane

FRANCIS TURBINE

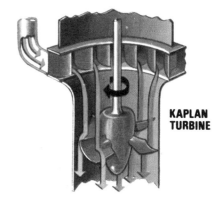

KAPLAN TURBINE

the bottom of the penstock to the outside. It opens above the highest level of the dam.

Some hydroelectric plants are able to store power. They have a pumped-storage system. When the demand for electricity is low, the turbines are not stopped. Instead the electricity is used to drive pumps. The pumps force water that has been through the turbines back up to the reservoir. This increases the head of water in the reservoir. It gives extra power when the demand for electricity is highest.

The largest hydroelectric plant in the United States is at the Grand Coulee Dam on the Columbia River. It produces more than 6,400 megawatts. The plant at Krasnoyarsk in the U.S.S.R. produces about 6,000 megawatts of power. A plant in South America will eventually produce 12,000 megawatts.

Hydroelectric schemes have several advantages over other means of producing power. They do not use fuel. The turbines and other equipment are fairly simple and reliable. Once they are built, they need little maintenance. Few men are needed to run them. Many plants are run almost completely automatically. *See also* TIDAL POWER.

D.M.H.W./R.W.L.

HYDROFOIL (hī′ drə fòil′) A hydrofoil is a structure on a motorboat which is designed to lift it out of the water as it gains speed. Trans-portation by water is usually much slower than transportation by land or air. A boat uses up most of its power overcoming the drag (resistance) of the water on its hull. For example, speedboats are designed so that they gradually lift out of the water as they increase speed. This reduces the area of hull in contact with the water, therefore reducing the drag. Heavier vessels cannot do this.

Hydrofoils are of such a shape that the flow of the water over them causes lift. (*See* AERODYNAMICS.) As the boat's speed increases, the hull lifts farther and farther out of the water until it is clear. The only parts then in contact with the water are the hydrofoils and supporting struts and the propeller shaft. Hydrofoils are of various designs. Some boats have V-shaped, or surface-piercing hydrofoils. Some have fully submerged foils. Others have variable-incidence (variable angle) foils that can be adjusted. In this way, the lift obtained is just enough to raise the hull of the boat out of the water.

Hydrofoil boats can travel very fast. They have the added advantage of making very little wash. One of the world's biggest hydrofoil boats is the U.S. Navy's AGEH-1. This boat has a service speed of 50 knots (93 kph or 57 mph).

The power units in most hydrofoil boats are diesel engines. But many of the latest craft

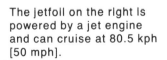

The jetfoil on the right is powered by a jet engine and can cruise at 80.5 kph [50 mph].

have gas turbine engines. Turbine engines are better suited to high-speed operation. Propulsion is generally by propellers which may be mounted on a separate shaft at the rear of the foils. For high-speed operation, specially designed propellers must be used. Propulsion may also be water-jet units driven by gas turbines and located at the base of the after foils, as in the Boeing PGH-2 Tucumcari naval patrol craft. Civil hydrofoils are in service in many countries, especially Scandinavia and the Soviet Union. J.J.A./R.W.L.

HYDROGEN (hī′ drə jən) Hydrogen is the first and simplest of all the elements. Its atomic number is 1, and it has the chemical symbol H. Hydrogen is a colorless, odorless, tasteless gas. Its atomic weight is 1.00797. At very low temperatures it becomes a solid. Solid hydrogen melts into a liquid at −259.2°C [−434.5°F]. At −252.8°C [−423°F], liquid hydrogen boils and becomes hydrogen gas. Hydrogen has a valence of 1 in all its compounds. (*See* VALENCE.)

Hydrogen is the most abundant element in

Hydrogen forms a large part of the stars, including this Trifid nebula in Sagittarius.

the universe. The sun and stars are made mostly of hydrogen. The gas is also spread very thinly throughout space. On earth, very little hydrogen gas is found. This is because the element is so reactive. It readily forms compounds with other elements. The most plentiful compound of hydrogen on earth is water. Each water molecule contains two hydrogen atoms linked to an oxygen atom. The formula for water is H_2O. Some hydrogen gas is found in natural gas. The gas is also found in the upper atmosphere.

All living things contain compounds of hydrogen. Hydrogen is found in carbohydrates, proteins, fats, and oils. Coal, petroleum, and natural gas all contain hydrogen compounds. They are mainly in the form of hydrocarbons. They were formed from the fossilized remains of plants that grew many millions of years ago. (*See* HYDROCARBON.)

Hydrogen gas can easily be made in the laboratory. Bubbles of the gas are formed when a metal such as zinc, sodium, or aluminum is added to dilute hydrochloric or sulfuric acid. Any metal above hydrogen in the electromotive series will replace hydrogen in the acids. (*See* ELECTROMOTIVE SERIES.)

Large amounts of hydrogen are produced for industry. The gas can be produced by treating natural gas, or gases from petroleum refining, with steam. The hydrocarbons are turned into hydrogen and carbon monoxide. Another method of production is the Bosch process. In this mixture of steam and carbon monoxide is passed over a catalyst. Hydrogen and carbon dioxide are formed. (*See* CATALYST.)

Very pure hydrogen can be produced by electrolysis. When an electric current is passed through water, the water splits up into the gases hydrogen and oxygen. Pure water will not conduct electricity. A little acid or alkali is added to it so that a current will pass.

Two-thirds of the hydrogen made in industry goes to make the gas ammonia. Ammonia is a compound of nitrogen and hydrogen. Its formula is NH_3. The process used to make ammonia is called the Haber process. (*See* HABER, FRITZ.) A large amount of hydrogen is also used to produce methanol. Different kinds of fuel can be made by treating coal, heavy oils, tar, and pitch with hydrogen. This process is called hydrogenation. It can also be used to change liquid vegetable oils into solid fats. This is known as the hardening of oils. Margarine is made in this way.

Hydrogen is extremely flammable. When it is mixed with oxygen, it forms an explosive mixture. The mixture is easily ignited. When hydrogen burns, great heat is produced. The gas is used in oxyhydrogen blowtorches to cut through and weld metal. Hydrogen can be used as a fuel. It makes a good fuel because burning it does not cause pollution. When hydrogen burns in air, only water is formed.

Hydrogen and oxygen are used in the rocket engines of spacecraft. They are also used to provide electricity and drinking water in these craft. They can be used in fuel cells. (*See* FUEL CELL.)

Hydrogen is the lightest element because its atoms are the simplest. The nucleus of a hydrogen atom is simply a proton, with a positive charge. In orbit around the nucleus is one electron, with a negative charge. If the electron is removed, the result is a hydrogen ion (H+). Acids contain hydrogen ions. (*See* ACID.)

Two hydrogen atoms come together to form a hydrogen molecule. They share their electrons between them. A hydrogen molecule is written H_2.

Hydrogen has two other isotopes. They are called deuterium and tritium. (*See* DEUTERIUM.) In deuterium, there is a neutron as well as a proton in the nucleus. A little deuterium is found mixed with ordinary hydrogen. If deuterium replaces the ordinary hydrogen in water, the result is heavy water. Its molecules are heavier than ordinary water because of the extra neutrons. Tritium contains three particles in its nucleus. There is

one proton and two neutrons. Tritium is an artificial isotope and is radioactive, but a minute amount occurs naturally. The normal form of hydrogen is sometimes called the protium isotope of hydrogen.

The sun and the stars produce vast amounts of energy from hydrogen. Atoms of hydrogen join together to form atoms of heavier elements. This is called fusion. During fusion, nuclear energy is released. For fusion to take place, the temperature must be very high. We rely on the fusion of hydrogen in the sun for the heat and light and all the energy that keeps us alive. *See also* FUSION.

D.M.H.W./J.R.W.

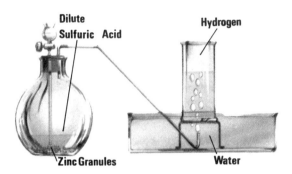

Apparatus for freeing hydrogen from sulphuric acid. Sulphuric acid reacts with zinc, releasing free hydrogen and forming zinc sulphate.

HYDROGEN BOND (hī' drə jən bänd') A hydrogen bond is a special chemical bond. It links hydrogen atoms inside molecules with other atoms. The other atoms may be in the same or in different molecules. Examples of hydrogen bonds are found between water molecules. Each water molecule contains two hydrogen atoms and one oxygen atom. The hydrogen atoms of each molecule have a positive electric charge. The oxygen atom has a negative electric charge. It attracts the positively charged electrons of the hydrogen atoms closer to it.

Opposite electric charges always attract each other. So the positively charged hydrogen atoms are attracted to the oxygen atoms of nearby water molecules. The water molecules cluster together in tight groups.

They are said to be joined by hydrogen bonds. This is the reason that water stays a liquid at ordinary temperatures. If the hydrogen bonds were not there the water molecules would separate. They drift away as water vapor. When water is heated, the water molecules move about more energetically. The hydrogen bonds are broken, and the water turns from liquid into vapor. Water molecules often link to other molecules by hydrogen bonds. They may form water of crystallization. (*See* HYDRATE.)

Hydrogen bonds are important in biochemistry. The twisted strands of the DNA molecule are held together by hydrogen bonds between the strands. (*See* NUCLEIC ACID.)

D.M.H.W./A.D.

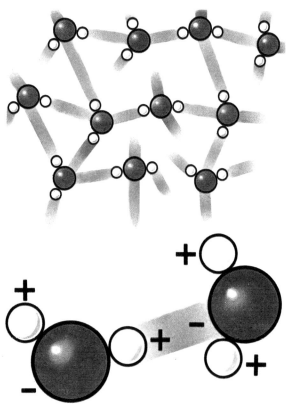

Hydrogen atoms have a positive electrical charge; oxygen atoms have a negative charge. These unlike charges attract each other.

HYDROGEN PEROXIDE (hī′ drə jən pə räk′ sīd′) Hydrogen peroxide is a colorless, syrupy liquid. Each molecule contains two atoms of hydrogen and two atoms of oxygen. It has the formula H_2O_2. Its boiling point is 150.2°C [302°F], and it freezes at −0.43°C [31.2°F]. It is unstable. Sunlight and heat make it break up into water and oxygen.

Because it yields oxygen so readily, hydrogen peroxide is a strong oxidizing agent. (*See* OXIDATION AND REDUCTION.) It may set fire to some substances. Pure hydrogen peroxide causes blisters on the skin. It is sometimes used as a rocket propellant.

For most uses, hydrogen peroxide is diluted with water. A 6% solution is called 20-volume peroxide because it can give up 20 times its own volume of oxygen gas. The solution is used as a bleach for hair and textiles, and as a disinfectant. A 3% solution (10-volume peroxide) is often used as a mouthwash.

Hydrogen peroxide is produced by the action of sulfuric acid on barium peroxide. It can also be produced by electrolysis of ammonium sulfate solution or concentrated sulfuric acid. (*See* ELECTROLYSIS.)

D.M.H.W./A.D.

HYDROGEN SULFIDE (hī′ drə jən səl′ fīd′) Hydrogen sulfide is a colorless, poisonous gas. It has the formula H_2S. It solidifies at −85.5°C [121.9°F] and boils at −60.7°C [−77.3°F].

The gas has a strong odor of rotten eggs. This is because eggs and other animal and vegetable matter contain sulfur compounds. Hydrogen sulfide gas is formed from these compounds as they decay. The gas is also found in nature in the mineral water from sulfur springs, in the gases from volcanoes, and in some oil wells. Hydrogen sulfide in the air turns coins and metal objects black. A layer of metal sulfide forms over them.

Hydrogen sulfide can be made by treating ferrous sulfide with hydrochloric or sulfuric acid. (*See* KIPPS APPARATUS.) In the laboratory, the gas can be used to identify and separate substances. If it is bubbled through a solution of a metal salt, it often causes the metal sulfide to form. This can be separated from other substances. (*See* CHEMICAL ANALYSIS.) D.M.H.W./A.D.

HYDROLOGY (hī drӓl′ ə jē) Hydrology is the study of the surface and underground water found on the continents. Hydrologists are scientists who study water. They study what chemicals are found in water, the characteristics of water, and how water flows in rivers, pipes, and underground streams. By studying these things, the hydrologist can help engineers build canals, sewers, and roads that will not wash out during floods or heavy rains. The hydrologist also helps towns and cities to locate underground sources of water for domestic use. Hydrologists have learned a lot about floods. They have helped design and build many flood-control dams. By making a few measurements and using a formula, they can figure out how much water is held behind a dam and how much water is able to spill over the top. By studying the water cycle, hydrologists can learn where water comes from and where it goes. (*See* WATER CYCLE.) They also try to save water and prevent soil erosion. *See also* HYDRAULICS; HYDROELECTRIC POWER; WATER.

S.R.G./W.R.S.

Hydrologists study lake and river systems of the world. Of special interest to them is the Mississippi-Missouri system. Above: the Missouri River in Montana.

HYDROLYSIS (hī drӓl′ ə səs) Hydrolysis is a chemical reaction in which a substance is broken down by the action of water. During the reaction, the water itself divides into hydrogen ions (H+) and hydroxyl ions (OH−). The ions link up with different parts of the substance, and form new compounds.

Salts can be hydrolyzed. They form two new compounds. One is an acid, and the other is a base. Sodium carbonate, for example, forms carbonic acid and sodium hydroxide. Carbonic acid is only a weak acid, but sodium hydroxide is a strong base. The solution that forms will therefore be more basic, or alkaline. (*See* ALKALI; BASE.)

In organic chemistry, esters can be hydrolyzed to form organic acids and alcohols. Acids or bases may have to be added to make hydrolysis take place. When an ester is hydrolyzed by boiling with a base, it forms an alcohol and a salt of the organic acid. Soaps are made in this way. The process is called saponification.

Hydrolysis also occurs in the digestion of foods. Enzymes help to bring about the hydrolysis of food into simple compounds that our bodies can use. (*See* ENZYMES.)

D.M.H.W./A.D.

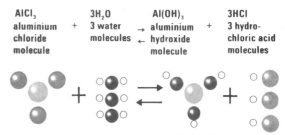

The hydrolysis of aluminum chloride into hydrochloric acid and aluminum hydroxide. As shown by the double arrows, the reaction is reversible.

HYDROMETER (hī drӓm′ ət ər) A hydrometer is an instrument that is used to make measurements of the relative density of liquids. (*See* RELATIVE DENSITY.) It is a glass tube with a weight on one end and numbers printed on the side. When the tube is set in

liquid, the bottom of it sinks into the liquid to a certain depth, depending upon the relative density of the liquid. The surface of the liquid reaches one of the numbers on the side. That number indicates the relative density of the liquid. If the tube sinks deeply, the liquid's surface reaches a number near the top of the tube, indicating a low relative density. If the tube sinks only a little, the liquid's surface reaches only the numbers at the bottom of the tube, indicating a high relative density. A hydrometer works on the principle that a floating body displaces its own weight in a liquid. (*See* ARCHIMEDES' PRINCIPLE.) Hydrometers are used in many different liquids to tell if they are pure.   S.R.G./R.W.L.

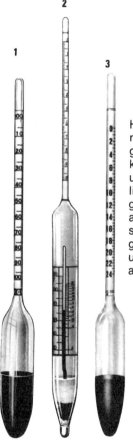

Hydrometers are used to measure the specific gravity of liquids. Different kinds of hydrometers are used for different kinds of liquids. Shown are: 1. a general purpose model; 2. a saccharometer for testing sugar solutions; 3. a general purpose model used for testing liquids that are heavier than water.

HYDROPONICS (hī′ drə pän′ iks) Hydroponics is the science of cultivating plants without soil. Instead of receiving nourish-ment from the soil, plants receive nourishment from water that has had nutrients (foods) added to it. Plants are grown in tanks containing gravel or coarse sand. The water is pumped through the gravel or sand periodically. Some plants are grown in tanks that contain only water. Hydroponics is also called soilless agriculture, nutriculture, and chemical culture. The science was developed in the 1800s, but it has never been used on a large scale by commercial growers.

Plants grown by this method must receive the same amount of light and warmth they would get if they were growing in soil. Growers who use hydroponic methods indoors must provide artificial light and heat.

There are two main methods of growing plants without soil, water culture and gravel culture.

Water culture is a method in which the plants are suspended with their roots in a tank of water. Nutrients like potassium nitrate, ammonium and aluminum sulfates, and calcium sulfate are added to the water. Manganous sulfate and ferrous sulfate are also added. Air is regularly pumped into the solution to replace air used up by the roots.

Gravel culture is a less complicated method of growing plants without soil. The plant roots are placed in coarse sand or gravel, and a nutrient solution is pumped through the material. In a variation of the gravel culture, the nutrient solution slowly drips from tiny tubes beside each plant. In this way, each plant can be fed more directly.

Scientists have not yet been able to prove that hydroponics produces better and larger crops. Some scientists have suggested that hydroponics would be ideal for growing crops in places were soil does not exist, like on ships at sea, frozen Arctic areas, and orbiting space stations.   W.R.P./F.W.S.

HYDROSTATICS (hī′ drə stat′ iks) Hydrostatics is one of the branches of physics that deal with the properties and behavior of

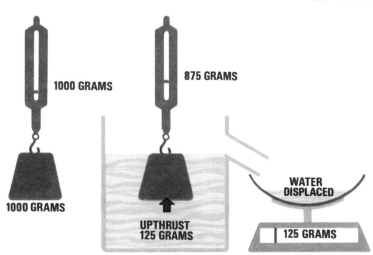

The first law of hydrostatics—Archimedes' principle—states that a floating or submerged object experiences an upthrust equal to the weight of the water it displaces. Right: a weight is hung from a scale. When immersed in water, the weight appears to weigh less. The weight of the water displaced equals the loss in weight.

1000 GRAMS

1000 GRAMS

875 GRAMS

WATER DISPLACED

UPTHRUST 125 GRAMS

125 GRAMS

liquids. It deals with liquids that are stationary. For example, it deals with water in a glass tank, the way the water presses against the sides, and the way anything floating in the tank behaves. The study of fluids that are moving is called hydrokinetics. Hydrostatics and hydrokinetics are linked together in the study of hydrodynamics.

In hydrostatics, there are three important principles, or laws that were discovered many years ago.

The first law The first law of hydrostatics deals with objects that are floating or immersed in liquids. It is also called Archimedes' principle. Archimedes was an ancient Greek scientist who discovered the principle over 2,200 years ago. The law states that a body floating or submerged in a liquid loses as much weight as the weight of the liquid that it displaces (pushes out of the way).

It is easy for us to tell that we lose weight when we are in water. It is also easy to see that we displace water. If a person climbs into an absolutely full bath, then a lot of water will spill over.

The principle is important in ships. When a ship has no cargo, it floats high in the water. It displaces only a little water. When it is heavily laden with cargo, it sinks much lower in the water. It displaces a greater amount of water. If the weight of the ship and the cargo

becomes greater than the weight of water the ship can displace, then the ship will sink.

The second law The second law of hydrostatics was stated in 1586 by the Dutch mathematician Simon Stevin. This law says that the pressure on a given point of a submerged body is equal to the weight of fluid directly above that point. A fluid may be a gas, or a mixture of gases, such as the atmosphere. This means that at the surface of the earth, the weight of several miles of atmosphere is pressing down upon us. High in the mountains, or higher still in airplanes, the pressure of the atmosphere is reduced.

At the deepest points in the ocean, the pressure is extremely great. Here there is the pressure of hundreds of meters of salt water as well as the atmospheric pressure on top of that. The pressure may be several tons per square centimeter.

The third law The third law of hydrostatics is also called Pascal's theorem. It was named for the French scientist Blaise Pascal. He discovered it in 1648. The law states that pressures applied to a contained liquid are transmitted equally throughout the liquid, in every direction.

The last two laws of hydrostatics are very important in engineering. Marine engineers, for example, must work out how strong to make the hulls of submarines to withstand underwater pressures. Dam-builders must be able to calculate how thick to build their dams. The laws are specially important in hydraulics. *See also* HYDRAULICS.

D.M.H.W./R.W.L.

HYDROXIDE (hī dräk′ sīd) A hydroxide is a chemical compound that contains a hydroxyl (–OH) group. Hydroxides can be thought of as compounds formed from water. One of the hydrogen atoms in H_2O has been changed for another atom, or group of atoms. In organic chemistry, there are many compounds with OH groups. However, these are usually called hydroxy compounds, not hydroxides.

Many, but not all hydroxides are bases. (*See* BASES.) Solutions of sodium and potassium hydroxides are very strong bases. The molecules split up in the water to give hydroxyl ions (OH–). Bases that dissolve in water are called alkalis. The most important alkali is sodium hydroxide. Other names for it are caustic soda and soda lye. Another important alkali is potassium hydroxide, or caustic potash.

A solution of calcium hydroxide is called limewater. It is used to detect carbon dioxide gas. When carbon dioxide is bubbled through it, the solution becomes milky. This is because white particles of calcium carbonate are formed.

Electrolysis plant for producing sodium hydroxide.

The hydroxides of certain metals may be produced by adding soluble hydroxides, such as sodium hydroxide, to soluble salts of the metal. For example, zinc hydroxide may be made by adding sodium hydroxide to zinc sulfate solution.

Soluble hydroxides may be made by electrolyzing solutions of salts. (*See* ELECTROLYSIS.) Sodium hydroxide forms during the electrolysis of sodium chloride (common salt) solution.

D.M.H.W./A.D.

HYENA (hī ē′ nə) Hyenas are doglike nocturnal carnivores that belong to the family Hyaenidae. Hyenas feed on the remains of dead animals. They also hunt animals for food. Hyenas have strong jaws and teeth, enabling them to crush and eat even large bones.

The spotted hyena (*Crocuta crocuta*) lives in Africa. Its fur is yellowish gray with black spots. It is known for its strange howl that sounds like a hysterical human laugh. The striped hyena (*Hyaena hyaena*) lives in northern Africa and parts of Asia. Smaller than the spotted hyena, the striped hyena has a grayish coat. Narrow black stripes run across its body and legs. The brown hyena (*Hyaena brunnea*) lives mainly in southern Africa. It has long hair on its back and stripes only on its legs. Frequently poisoned and shot by farmers, the brown hyenas are now endangered. *See also* AARDWOLF.

J.J.A./J.J.M.

HYGIENE (hī′ jēn′) Hygiene is the branch of science and medicine that has to do with maintaining a healthy body and mind. If a body is generally fit and healthy, it is much more able to withstand disease or to recover quickly from an illness or accident.

To keep healthy, the body has many needs. Among the most important are fresh air, light, warmth, cleanliness, and a balanced diet. The diet should consist of the right kinds of food and drink. Supplies of food and water must be fresh and clean, and therefore not contaminated with vermin. Regular washing, proper sanitation, proper sleep, and regular exercise all aid in personal health.

Although a person can do much to guard his health, some threats to health can be prevented by the action of communities. For example, governments enforce laws to control pollution of the air and water. Laws are also passed to protect workers in factories or other places from various hazards. Clean water supplies and the disposal of garbage and sewage are usually the responsibility of public utilities or authorities. Governmental bodies, such as the United States Food and Drug Administration, make sure hygienic standards are kept in food processing industries. (*See* FOOD PRESERVATION.) At the international level, the World Health Organization develops national programs to fight disease and prevent its spread. *See also* MEDICINE; MENTAL HEALTH; NUTRITION; SEWAGE TREATMENT. J.J.A./J.J.F.

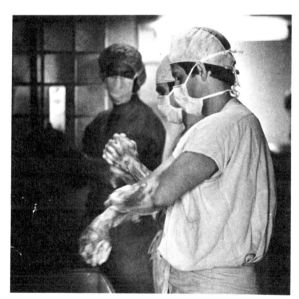

These doctors are scrubbing their hands — one of the hygienic measures essential in an operating room.

HYGROMETER (hī gräm′ ət ər) A hygrometer is an instrument that measures the water vapor content of the air. It is used by meteorologists to determine relative humidity. There are two main types of hygrometers:

the psychrometer and the hair hygrometer.

A psychrometer consists of two thermometers. One thermometer gives the actual temperature. The bulb of the other thermometer is wrapped in muslin and kept moist with water. In order to determine the humidity, the psychrometer is spun at about 14 km [9 mi] per hour. Water evaporates from the wet-bulb thermometer, thus lowering its temperature reading. (*See* EVAPORATION.) If the humidity is high, less water will evaporate.

The wet-bulb thermometer reading is always less than the dry-bulb reading, unless there is 100% relative humidity. The difference between the thermometer readings is called the wet-bulb depression. Using this information, the relative humidity can be determined by referring to special tables.

A hair hygrometer uses human hair to determine the humidity. The hair absorbs moisture from the air, becoming longer if the humidity is high. A lever moves according to the change in hair length, indicating the relative humidity. J.M.C./C.R.

HYPHA (hī′ fə) Hyphae are the threadlike parts of a fungus that make up the mycelium. A hypha can consist of one or more cells. It may branch out and join with another hypha to form a dikaryon, which may eventually permit sexual reproduction. On the other hand, the tip of a hypha may separate to form spores called conidia. These break off, germinate, and grow into new fungi by asexual reproduction. *See also* MOLD. W.R.P./E.R.L.

HYPNOSIS (hip nō′ səs) Hypnosis is a state in which the mind becomes less aware of the surrounding world. The subject (person under hypnosis) may seem to be asleep, but can still respond to outside events. Easily influenced by suggestion, the subject can control many body functions that are normally automatic. For example, a hypnotized person may be insensitive to pain if he or she is told that he feels nothing.

A person is generally put into a state of hypnosis by another person, called a hypnotist. But hypnosis can also be brought about by the subject himself. This is called self-hypnosis or autohypnosis.

If performed by a hypnotist, the hypnotist talks to the subject slowly, repeating his words over and over again. Eventually the subject is completely relaxed, and goes into a trance (a hypnotic state).

Not everyone can be hypnotized. People cannot be hypnotized against their wills. Subjects do not do anything under hypnosis that is against their ideas or principles. But hypnosis is not a game. It can be extremely dangerous when performed by an untrained person.

Hypnosis is often used in place of an anesthetic during surgery or childbirth. The patient feels nothing but can cooperate with the surgeon. Hallucinations can also be induced under hypnosis. A hypnotized person may be able to recall forgotten events in his early life. This ability has been used by psychiatrists to treat certain mental illnesses. *See also* PSYCHIATRY; PSYCHOANALYSIS. J.J.A./J.J.F.

HYSTERESIS (his′ tə rē′ səs) Hysteresis is a lag that occurs when an attempt is made to alter the magnetism of an object. To make a piece of iron magnetic, the iron can be placed in a strong magnetic field. (*See* FIELD; MAGNETISM.) As the strength of the field is increased, the magnetism of the iron grows. Eventually it cannot become any more magnetic. It is said to be saturated with magnetism. If the magnetic field is taken away, some of the magnetism in the iron remains.

To remove the magnetism from the iron, an opposite magnetic field must be applied. This field will have to reach a certain strength before the iron becomes nonmagnetic. If the strength of the field is increased as before, the iron will again become magnetic. Its magnetism will be in the opposite direction. Eventually it will again become saturated. However, there is always a lag between the change

in strength of the magnetic field and the change in magnetism of the iron. It is the resistance to change in magnetism that forms hysteresis.

The hysteresis that occurs with different substances can be measured. A hysteresis loop is drawn to show what happens as an object is gradually magnetized and then demagnetized. Soft iron is much easier to demagnetize than hard steel. The best permanent magnets are made of materials that are very difficult to demagnetize. They are made of specially produced alloys that provide wide hysteresis loops.

The hysteresis motor is a kind of electric motor that relies on hysteresis to keep a constant speed. A constant speed is needed specially in electric clocks and record players.

Hysteresis occurs in many systems. It is very important in elasticity, or the stretching properties of elastic bodies. D.M.H.W./J.T.

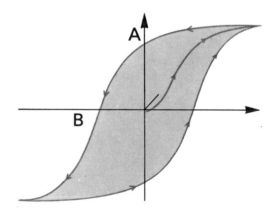

Plotting a graph of magnetometer deflection against increasing electric current put through an electromagnet gave this hysteresis loop. The magnetometer is deflected at A when when the core is magnetized. To demagnetize the core, the current must be reversed and increased to reach B.

IBIS (ī′ bəs) Ibises are tall birds that belong to the family Threskiornithidae. They are closely related to the herons. (*See* HERON.) Ibises have long necks, bills, and legs. They wade in shallow water and catch small fish, reptiles, and amphibians. There are four species of ibis in North America. Three species are found only in the southeastern part of the United States and parts of Mexico. The fourth species, the white-faced ibis, is found in west-central United States and Mexico. *See also* SPOONBILL.   S.R.G./M.L.

The scarlet ibis lives in tropical South America.

ICE (īs) Ice is the solid form of water. When water is cooled, it contracts (shrinks) until its temperature drops to 4°C [39°F]. It then expands until the temperature drops to 0°C [32°F], the freezing point of water. It remains ice until the temperature goes above the freezing point. It then melts, although the temperature of the water remains at 0°C [32°F] until all the ice has melted.

Ice has a greater volume than water, but its density is slightly less. This is why ice floats in a glass of water.

When ice freezes, hydrogen bonds form a rigid structure of six-sided crystals. The type of crystal structure depends on how the water is frozen. Forms of ice include snow, sleet, frost, and hail.   J.M.C./C.R.

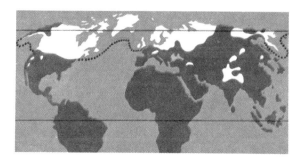

The maximal extent of glacial ice in the Ice Age.

ICE AGE (īs āj) An ice age was a period of the earth's history when large areas of the globe were covered by glaciers and ice sheets. The most recent ice age occurred during the Pleistocene epoch, which ended about 10,000 years ago. There is also evidence that other ice ages have occurred. An ice age took place during Precambrian times, about 600 million years ago. Another ice age occurred during the late Carboniferous and early Permian periods, about 280 million years ago, and this one affected all lands of the southern hemisphere.

The Pleistocene ice age   The last ice age began about 600,000 years ago during the Pleistocene epoch. The ice advanced southward during four periods called glacial ages. These glacial ages are separated by interglacial ages, when the ice retreated. The glacial ages, from oldest to most recent, are the Nebraskan, the Kansan, the Illinoian, and the Wisconsin. The interglacial ages are the Aftonian, the Yarmouth, and the Sangamon. A glacial age lasts about 40,000 to 60,000 years. Interglacial ages last about 40,000 years. Geologists have suggested that the earth may now be in an interglacial age.

Scientists have learned a great deal about the ice ages by studying fossils and other evidence from the Pleistocene epoch. Geologists believe that great ice sheets were centered near what is now Hudson Bay in North America and on the Scandinavian peninsula in Europe. The ice became thick, and flowed out from these centers. All of Canada and the northern third of the United States, as far south as New York City and the Missouri River valley, were covered by ice. In places, the ice was 2,400 to 3,000 m [8,000 to 10,000 ft] thick. In Europe, ice covered all of northern Europe, the British Isles, and much of northern Russia. At times during the Pleistocene epoch, more than 30% of the earth's surface was covered with ice.

The Pleistocene glaciations had a profound effect on the landscape of not only those areas affected by the ice cover but those directly south. Because the climatic zones were shifted southward, plants and animals were forced to live in more restricted environments. Fjords, moraines, and drumlins were created by the retreating ice. Many lakes, including the Great Lakes, were formed during the last ice age.

Different theories have been proposed to explain what causes ice ages. Some scientists believe that changes in oceanic circulation patterns caused by continental drift had world-wide cooling effects that encouraged growth of glaciers and ice caps. Others think that in the 300 million years it takes for the solar system to make a complete rotation of the galaxy, there are two phases 150 million years apart, in which the galactic environment has a cooling influence. And other astronomers have found evidence that cyclic variations in the earth's orbit can produce cooling effects strong enough to start an ice age.   J.M.C./W.R.S.

ICEBERG (īs' bərg') An iceberg is a large, floating mass of ice. Icebergs break away, or calve, from the glaciers and ice sheets along the coasts of Greenland and Antarctica. They sometimes present a major hazard to shipping.

A glacier often extends slightly into the sea. Eventually, cracks form in the ice, and a piece of the glacier breaks off, perhaps during stormy weather. Greenland is the source of most North Atlantic icebergs. These icebergs may be taller than 90 m [300 ft]. Antarctic icebergs are often very large, but are usually flat-topped. One huge Antarctic iceberg had an area of 31,000 sq km [12,000 sq mi].

Usually, only one-ninth of an iceberg is visible above water. As an iceberg floats, some of the ice melts and pieces break off. Eventually, it completely disappears.

In 1912, the British ocean liner Titanic hit an iceberg and sank in the North Atlantic. More than 1,500 people died. Since then, the United States and other countries have formed an International Ice Patrol. The patrol, operated by the United States Coast Guard, uses ships, planes, and radar to locate icebergs. *See also* GLACIATION.   J.M.C./W.R.S.

ICELAND SPAR (ī' slənd spär') Iceland spar is a transparent variety of calcite. It is so called because Iceland is the chief source of this mineral. Iceland spar has the property of double refraction. This means that if a piece of this mineral is placed over a line of type in a book, for instance, a person sees "double." Instead of one line of type, he sees two. The property of double refraction makes it possible to use Iceland spar to produce polarized light. (*See* POLARIZED LIGHT.)   J.J.A./R.H.

ICHNEUMON FLY (ik nü' mən flī) Ichneumon flies are insects belonging to the same group as bees and wasps (order Hymenoptera). Ichneumon flies are not true flies. They have four membranous wings. Flies have only two. Some types of this insect are about the size of a small ant. Others grow to 6 cm [2.3 in] in length, including the ovipositor. They do not sting people.

The female's body ends in a pointed egg-laying tool called an ovipositor. The ovipositor may be up to twice the length of the body. The three threadlike parts of this organ form a tube. With it, the insect places eggs in the bodies of caterpillars or other larvae and pupae. The parasitic larvae remain where they are placed until full grown. The larvae often kill the insect on which they live as parasites.

Ichneumon flies are important to farmers. The insects often feed on other insects that destroy plants. The ichneumon fly larvae eats insects in the egg, larval, and pupal stages. Ichneumon flies destroy caterpillars especially. These insects also attack spiders and the larvae of certain beetles, flies, and wasps.

J.J.A./J.E.R.

An ichneumon fly, a relative of bees and wasps.

ICHTHYOLOGY (ik′ thē äl′ ə jē) The study of fishes is called ichthyology. It includes the study of the bodies of fishes, the evolution of fishes, how and where the fishes live, and their relationships to other fishes and animals. Ichthyologists, people who study fishes, do many different things. Some ichthyologists study only the fish itself. They cut open the body and learn how it is put together. Other ichthyologists travel all over the world studying where the thousands of different kinds of fishes live. Besides learning about the fishes, the scientists learn a lot about how the earth used to be. Still other ichthyologists study the number of fishes that live in certain places. They start programs to help increase the numbers of fishes. They also help fishermen so that they may catch more fish. Many scientists decide how many fish can be caught without hurting the whole population of fishes. *See also* CONSERVATION.

S.R.G./E.C.M.

ICHTHYOSAUR (ik′ thē ə sȯr′) An ichthyosaur was a fishlike reptile that lived in the Mesozoic era. (*See* MESOZOIC ERA.) It became extinct at the end of that era. There have been many fossils of ichthyosaurs found. They resembled the sharks of today, except they had a long beaklike mouth with many sharp teeth. *See also* FISH; FOSSIL; REPTILE; SHARK.

S.R.G./E.C.M.

ICONOSCOPE (ī kän′ ə skōp′) Iconoscope is the name given to the cathode-ray tube that first made television transmission possible. The iconoscope was invented in the early 1900s by Vladimir K. Zworykin, a Russian physicist. The iconoscope is shaped like a light bulb. It has a thin neck, but it is usually much larger than a light bulb.

Light enters the lens of the television camera, and is focused on a photoelectric surface inside the tube. The photoelectric surface changes the light rays into electrical impulses. The photoelectric surface is made up of tiny, light-sensitive beads spread on a sheet of mica. An electron gun is enclosed in the neck of the tube. The gun sprays a stream of electrons across the photoelectric surface. The amount of light that falls on the surface causes the amount of positive electric charge on the surface to vary. And the beams of light

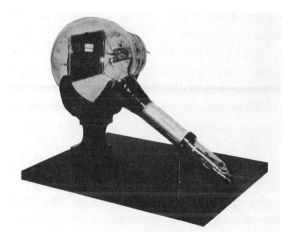

Iconoscope (above) was a type of cathode ray tube used in early television cameras.

coming through the television lens are changed to electric charges. These charges become the electric waves that make up the broadcast.

The image orthicon has replaced the iconoscope in today's television broadcasting. It is much smaller, and more sensitive to light. Thus, it allows television cameras to operate in conditions where the lighting is dim.   W.R.P./J.T.

IDEAL MECHANICAL ADVANTAGE A
certain force is needed to lift an object. A machine allows you to use less force than if you lifted it on your own. Some machines, such as a pulley, can be used to lift objects. The ratio of the weight lifted to the force needed is called the mechanical advantage (mi kan' i kəl əd vant' ij) of the machine. The mechanical advantage is always greater than one. For a simple machine, the mechanical advantage can be calculated. The calculated mechanical advantage is called the ideal mechanical advantage. In practice, the mechanical advantage is always less than the ideal mechanical advantage. This means that, in practice, a slightly greater force is needed to lift an object. This difference is due mainly to friction. (*See* FRICTION.)   M.E./J.T.

IGNEOUS ROCK (ig' nē əs räk') Igneous
rock forms from the cooling and crystallization of a hot, molten material called magma. Magma is molten rock that has been subjected to great temperature and pressure beneath the earth's surface. There are two main types of igneous rock: extrusive and intrusive.

Extrusive rock is magma forced from the earth's interior through a volcano or a crack in the earth's surface. This magma, called lava when it reaches the earth's surface, quickly cools when it is exposed to air. Because of the rapid cooling, extrusive rock contains small crystals and is fine-textured. Extrusive igneous rocks include basalt, obsidian, and pumice.

Intrusive rock forms when magma cools below the surface and in pre-existing rock forms. The magma sometimes cools in large masses called batholiths. It may also cool in vertical bands called dikes or in horizontal layerlike bands called sills. Because intrusive rock cools and hardens slowly, it contains large crystals and is coarse-textured. Granite is an intrusive igneous rock.

Igneous rocks contain a variety of minerals, including quartz, mica, and feldspar.
J.M.C./W.R.S.

The basalt rocks (above) are examples of extrusive rock. The granite rocks (below) are examples of intrusive rock.

IGUANA (ig wän' ə) An iguana is a large
lizard that belongs to the family Iguanidae. There are many different species of iguanas in the world. Most of them live in South America and on islands in the Pacific Ocean. The best-known species of iguana is one living on the Galapagos Islands. It may reach a

length of 1.5 m [5 ft]. Named the marine iguana, it is the only marine lizard in the world. *See also* LIZARD; REPTILE.

S.R.G./R.L.L.

ILLUMINATION (il ü′ mə nā′ shən) Illumination is the creation of artificial light. The earliest means of illumination were open fires and burning torches. Candles, kerosene lamps and lanterns, and gas lamps were developed later. Incandescent electric lights were introduced in 1879 by Thomas Edison. Today, most of our illumination is accomplished with incandescent lights. (*See* INCANDESCENCE.)

The neon light, developed in 1911 by French physicist Georges Claude, is used largely to illuminate commercial signs and displays. The fluorescent lamp is one of the most recent developments in illumination. It produces a brighter light than an incandescent bulb. Fluorescent bulb tubes are straight or curved. They are used to light office buildings and other commercial and public structures. (*See* FLUORESCENCE.) Sodium and mercury vapor lamps are used to illuminate highways and other outdoor public areas.

In photometry, illumination is the luminous flux incident per unit area expressed in lumens per unit of area. (*See* PHOTOMETRY.) *See also* ELECTRIC LIGHT. W.R.P./J.T.

IMAGINARY NUMBER (im aj̄′ ə nər′ ē nəm′ bər) If a number is multiplied by itself, the result is another number. This number is the square of the first number. The first number is the square root of the second number. If the square root is positive, then so is the square. If the square root is negative, then the square is still positive. This is because a negative times a negative gives a positive. This means that both positive and negative numbers give a positive number when squared. What, then, is the square root of a negative number? A special number has to be used. Its symbol is i and it is the square root of minus one, $\sqrt{-1}$. Suppose you want to know the square root of -16. The square root of $+16$ is 4 (or -4). Therefore, the square root of -16 can be written as 4i. The square of 4i is $4 \times i \times 4 \times i$. This equals $4 \times 4 \times i \times i$. 4×4 is 16 and $i \times i$ is $\sqrt{-1} \times \sqrt{-1}$ which is -1. Therefore, the square of 4i is -1×16 which equals -16. Numbers such as i and 4i are called imaginary numbers. M.E./S.P.A.

IMMISCIBLE LIQUID (im is′ ə bəl lik′ wəd) Two liquids are immiscible if they cannot be mixed together. A common example is oil and water. If you try to mix them together, a boundary forms between the two. The lighter liquid, usually the oil, lies above the heavier liquid. Certain liquids, such as ethyl alcohol and water, can be mixed together. They are said to be miscible. Whether two

Iguanas are found mainly in tropical parts of the Americas. Below: the marine iguana.

liquids mix or not depends on their chemical properties. If they resemble each other chemically, they are usually miscible. For example, the molecules of both water and alcohol have an –OH group. Because of this, they are miscible. On the other hand, water and oil are very different chemically and so are immiscible.   M.E./A.D.

Vaccination (above) is one of the ways to make the human body immune to disease.

IMMUNITY (im yü′ nət ē) Immunity is the ability of the body to resist certain harmful substances that enter it. The substances include disease-producing organisms such as bacteria and viruses. The human body has natural immunity to many bacteria and viruses that cause disease in other creatures. Other diseases attack the body. The body's defenses work to overcome them. In this way, the body can gain immunity. If the body builds up a permanent defense, disease cannot attack that body again for a long period. In some cases, the immunity lasts for the rest of a person's life.

Through immunization, a person can be given immunity to many diseases without first catching the disease. Immunization is any medical procedure that makes a person able to develop immunity to specific disease-producing organisms. (*See* VACCINATION.)

The job of fighting invading germs, such as bacteria, is chiefly carried out by the lymphatic system and the lymphocytes. The lymphocytes are a type of white blood cell produced in lymphatic tissue. The action of the lymphocytes depends on their recognition of the invading germs as ''foreign.'' By some method that is not properly understood, the lymphocytes react to the presence of any protein that does not belong to the body itself. This includes the proteins that make up germs. This type of reaction is called an immune reaction.

The lymphocytes deal with the foreign protein, called antigen, by producing antibodies. Some antigens produce poisons called toxins. In order to neutralize these toxins, the lymphocytes produce a kind of antibody called antitoxin. Both antitoxins and antibodies are highly specific. In other words, they can fight only a particular type of disease-producing germ, or a few types that are very closely related. This is why catching chicken pox does not give immunity to smallpox. However, catching cowpox does give immunity to smallpox. The viruses that cause cowpox and smallpox are very similar.

The production of antibodies is too slow to stop invading germs that cause disease the first time they enter the body. But they may continue to circulate in the blood, ready to react immediately if infection occurs again. In other cases, the body may be able to make the antibody much more quickly a second time. This is why the common diseases of childhood, such as mumps, chicken pox, and measles, usually strike only once. Such acquired immunity is called active immunity. The body has actively produced its own antibodies. Immunity can also be passive. In this way, the body can acquire ready-made antibodies. A baby acquires immunity to many diseases in this way. It absorbs antibodies from its mother's bloodstream before birth and from her milk afterwards. Such protection, however, is short-lived.

Artificial immunity through vaccination may also be active or passive. Active immunity can be acquired by injecting dead germs into the body, or injecting a type of the living germ that causes only a slight discomfort. In some cases, a toxoid is used. A toxoid is a bacterial poison that has been made harmless. Each of these methods may stimulate the body to make antibodies or antitoxins.

Passive immunity is given by injecting a serum. (*See* INJECTION.) This is obtained from the blood of an infected person or animal that has produced the right antibodies.

In the case of most diseases caused by viruses, vaccination remains medicine's basic weapon. Diseases caused by viruses range from a common cold to smallpox and polio. These viruses are unaffected by antibiotics and the sulfa drugs. But in 1957 it was discovered that the body has a second type of immune response to viruses apart from that involving antibodies. It was found that body cells attacked by viruses make a substance called interferon. Interferon passes to neighboring cells, helping them to resist the spread of the viruses. If has been found that interferon from a particular species protects any creature of the same species from most types of viruses. But it does not protect any other species. Therefore human patients can only be protected with human interferon. This would be effective against a wide range of virus diseases.

The body's immune response to foreign protein is not always a help to medicine. The same mechanism is responsible for rejecting tissue transplanted from another person's body into a patient. (*See* TRANSPLANTATION.) The lymphocytes attack a transplanted heart or kidney in the same way as they attack invading bacteria.

Some diseases occur because of deficiencies in the body's immune system, called immunodeficiencies. Most scientists believe that a newborn child does not have the ability to reject foreign tissues. Its body learns this in the first year or two of life. At the same time, it learns not to attack its own tissues. If the body's ability to recognize its own tissues is somehow disrupted, an autoimmune disease may result. An autoimmune disease, such as multiple sclerosis, is a form of disease caused when the body's defense mechanism against infection begins to attack the body's own tissues. In quite another way, if the body becomes oversensitive to foreign proteins, the result may be an allergy, such as asthma or hay fever.   J.J.A./J.J.F.

IMPACT (im′ pakt′) Impact, in mechanics, is the striking of one body against another. In an automobile crash, impact happens at the moment of collision between the auto and another object. A law involving impact states that the total momentum (velocity times mass) of the bodies is the same before and after impact if both objects are elastic, and not effected by other forces.

In actual practice, some of the energy of momentum is absorbed while causing a permanent change in one, or both, of the bodies. The denting that occurs when two autos collide is an example of this. Since the mass of both bodies remains the same, the impact must result in a loss of velocity. The ratio between the differences of the velocities of the two bodies after impact to the same differences before impact is called the impact coefficient.   W.R.P./J.T.

IMPALA (im pal′ ə) The impala (*Aepyceros melampus*) is an African antelope known for its tremendous jumping ability. High jumps of more than 3 m [10 ft] and long jumps of 9 m [30 ft] have been recorded. Impalas are also swift runners. They may run as fast as 80 km [50 mi] per hour.

Standing from 84 to 94 cm [33 to 37 in] at the shoulder, impalas weigh from 45 to 82 kg

These impalas live in the bush country of southern and eastern Africa.

[100 to 180 lbs]. The animals have glossy, reddish brown coats on the top and sides. The tail and underparts are white. The male has a pair of slender horns up to 91 cm [3 ft] in length. The strongest males lead harem herds. These herds are made up of females and young. The other males live alone or stay together in bachelor herds.

Impalas live in many areas of East and South Africa. They rarely venture far from water. Impalas prefer bush country, where there is plenty of shelter. Their natural enemies include leopards, lions, and wild African hunting dogs. The impalas feed mainly on grass, leaves, and fruit.   J.J.A./J.J.M.

IMPEDANCE (im pēd′ əns) Suppose that a battery is connected to an electric cicuit. The battery causes a potential difference to be set up between the two ends of the circuit. (*See* POTENTIAL.) This produces a current in the circuit. The size of the current depends on the size of the potential difference. It also depends on the components and the wire in the circuit. They always oppose the flow of current. If the current is a direct current, then it flows in one direction only. (*See* DIRECT CURRENT.) The opposition of a component or a wire is then called its resistance. (*See* RESISTANCE, ELECTRICAL.) If the current is an alternating current, its direction reverses at short intervals. (*See* ALTERNATING CURRENT.) The opposition to the flow is slightly different in this case and so it has a different name. It is called the impedance.

M.E./L.L.R.

IMPLANTATION (im′ plan′ tā′ shən) Implantation is the process in most mammals by which a fertilized egg, or zygote, attaches itself to the uterine wall. (*See* UTERUS.) The wall of the uterus prepares for the arrival of the fertilized egg by becoming thickened with blood, water, and nutrients. (*See* MENSTRUAL CYCLE.) These changes take place because of the action of the female sex hormone progesterone.

When the fertilized egg touches the uterine wall, the egg burrows into the thickened tissue. The zygote stays embedded in the wall until birth. During this time, the embryo relies on the uterine lining for the environment it needs in which to grow and develop properly.

The term implantation is also used to describe the surgical insertion of a mechanical device or an artificial organ into the body of a living organism. (*See* TRANSPLANTATION.) *See also* GESTATION PERIOD; PREGNANCY; REPRODUCTIVE SYSTEM; SEX.   A.J.C./J.J.F.

IMPLOSION (im plō′ zhən) Implosion is the reverse of explosion. (*See* EXPLOSIVE.) An implosion occurs when a vessel collapses inward. This is caused by a difference in the air pressures outside and inside the vessel. Normally, the atmosphere pushes against both the inside and outside walls of an open flask with equal pressure. If, however, the neck of the flask is connected to a pump, and the air inside is gradually taken out, the internal pressure will decrease. Eventually, the pressure outside would be so great compared to the pressure inside that the flask would collapse inward, or implode.

A cathode-ray tube used in electronics contains a partial vacuum. When the tube is cracked, it usually implodes with great violence. The cracking weakens the wall of the tube, and the external pressure causes it to burst inward toward the lower pressure.   W.R.P./J.T.

INCAN CIVILIZATION (ing′ kən siv′ ə lə zā′ shən) The Incan civilization flourished in South America many years before the arrival of European explorers. The Inca Empire extended 4,020 km [2,500 mi] along the Pacific Ocean. Cuzco, the Inca capital, was located in the Andes mountains.

The Incas had a highly organized gov-

ernment that directed the everyday lives of the citizens. Their main occupation was farming. The Incas were the first people to raise potatoes. They farmed the steep hillsides of the Andes, growing crops like squash, maize, beans, peanuts, cotton, and tomatoes.

The Incas domesticated the llama, using it for its wool and as a beast of burden. They ate llama and guinea pig meat, as well as the many vegetables they grew.

The Incas invented a calendar of considerable accuracy. Their year started on December 21, the summer solstice in the southern hemisphere. Their year was divided into 12 months of 30 days each. Each month was divided into three weeks of ten days each.

The Incas were great builders. They built a superb network of roads throughout the empire. Messengers relayed news by running between stations located at intervals along the roads. Rope suspension bridges hung over deep chasms.

Incas built magnificent temples and palaces out of stone. They also built irrigation canals to maintain an adequate water supply. The Incan civilization collapsed soon after the arrival of Europeans in the western hemisphere. Much of the rich culture of the Incas was lost.   J.M.C./S.O.

INCANDESCENCE (in′ kən des′ əns) Incandescence is the emission of visible light by any object at high temperature. An object at low temperature radiates infrared light, which is not visible to the human eye. (*See* SPECTRUM.) An object being heated starts to become incandescent when it gives off red light. Other colors are emitted until only white light is given off. The color is a good indication of the temperature. Red light indicates a lower temperature than white light.

Most artificial lighting in homes and offices is incandescent. In 1880, the first electric light bulbs using the principle of incandescence were produced. *See also* LUMINESCENCE.   J.M.C./J.T.

INCENSE CEDAR (in' sens' sēd' ər) The incense cedar is a tree that is not a cedar but a member of the cypress family. It grows to heights greater than 30 m [100 ft]. It has dark green leaves that grow in overlapping groups of four pairs. The cones are less than 2.5 cm [1 in] long, and have six scales. Four of the scales carry one or two winged seeds.

Incense cedars grow in California and Oregon. Its fragrant wood is used in carpentry.   J.M.C./M.H.S.

INDIAN CIVILIZATION (in' dē ən siv' ə lə zā' shən) The Indians of the Western Hemisphere are the true native Americans. Christopher Columbus named them "Indians" when he arrived in the New World because he thought he had reached India.

The ancestors of the Indians probably came to the Americas during the ice age. At that time, the ocean level dropped because of glaciation, exposing land that is now underwater. The Indians' ancestors probably crossed a land bridge from Asia, where the Bering Strait is now. From there, the Indians moved southward throughout North and South America. When the Europeans arrived in the New World, most of the Indians lived in small villages and subsisted by hunting and fishing. The major Indian political states were, however, limited to Central and South America. These areas still have a large Indian population. Many of them have intermarried with Europeans and some with Africans.

The situation in North America was quite different. Most Indians had their land taken away by the white settlers. The Indians were continually pushed further west as the white settlements expanded. Today, many North American Indians still live on reservations, although increasing numbers live off reservations in urban centers and elsewhere.

Contributions of the Indians   The Indians made countless contributions to the society of the United States. Many Indian words are used to describe places and things. More than half of the states' names are Indian words, such as Connecticut, Massachusetts, and Illinois. Many names of American cities, like Miami and Cheyenne, are Indian words.

The Indians introduced Europeans to new foods such as corn, avocados, cacao, peanuts, peppers, potatoes, pumpkins, and tomatoes. The Indians also cultivated tobacco.

Indians developed a number of kinds of canoes, which were their most common means of water travel. There were large dugout canoes, bark canoes, and light boats made of reeds. The Indians of the north were the first people to use toboggans and snowshoes. Indians also played games that have since evolved into lacrosse and field hockey.

The Indians made important contributions to the field of medicine. The Incas used cocaine, derived from the coca plant, for medicinal purposes. Other tribes used quinine to fight malaria and curare to fight tetanus. *See also* INCAN CIVILIZATION; MAYAN CIVILIZATION.   J.M.C./S.O.

INDICATOR (in' də kāt' ər) Indicators are substances that are used by chemists to show when a chemical reaction has finished. The most common use for indicators is in reactions between acids and bases. (*See* ACID; BASE.) Acids and bases react together to form a salt and water. They are said to neutralize each other. The strength of an acid or a base is measured by its pH. (*See* PH.) Water has a pH of 7. An acid has a pH of less than 7. The more acidic the solution, the lower the pH. Bases have a pH of between 7 and 14. The stronger the base, the higher the pH.

The most common kind of indicator is a dye that changes color over a range of pH. An example is a purple dye called litmus. (*See* LITMUS.) Litmus is red in an acidic solution and blue in a basic solution. Suppose that a few drops of litmus are added to a base. An acidic solution is slowly added. When enough acid has been added, the solution turns pink

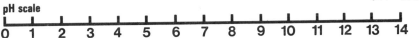

A table of some indicators used in chemical analysis, shows the pH range (degree of acidity) at which they change color.

because of the litmus. All indicators react with the compounds being tested. Litmus reacts with a base to form a blue dye and with acid to form a red dye. When the acid is added to the base, they immediately react together. Eventually the base is neutralized by the acid. When a little extra acid is added, it reacts with the litmus. Therefore the color of the solution changes from blue to red.

Indicators are frequently used to find out the strength of a solution. Suppose that the acid solution has a certain, known strength. The volume of acid added can be measured and so can the volume of the basic solution. Then the strength of the base can be calculated. Litmus changes color over a wide range of pH and so is only suitable for strong acids and bases. Other indicators are more accurate since they change color over a smaller range. A universal indicator is a mixture of different indicators. Its color changes throughout the pH scale. It is used to make a quick and rough guess of the pH of a solution. A different kind of indicator is the precipitation indicator. Precipitation is when a chemical reaction causes a solid to form quickly in a reaction. *(See* PRECIPITATION.) Precipitation indicators produce a precipitation when the reaction is completed.

Indicators are also used in oxidation-reduction reactions. *(See* OXIDATION AND RE-DUCTION.) They are called oxidation-reduction indicators, or redox indicators. They work in the same way. The indicator is one color when it is oxidized and a different color when it is reduced. M.E./A.D.

INDIGO (in′ di gō′) Indigo is a deep blue dye used to color cotton and wool. The pigment in indigo is called indigotin. This dye was once obtained from several plants, especially the indigo plant. The indigo plant, which grows chiefly in India, is a member of the pea family. Indigo is now made artificially. Synthetic indigo is a dye called alizarin. *See also* DYE.
J.J.A./J.D.

INDIUM (in′ dē əm) Indium (In) is a very soft, silvery white metallic element. The atomic number of indium is 49 and its atomic weight is 114.82. Its melting point is 156.6°C [313.9°F] and it boils at 2,080°C [3776°F]. Its relative density is 7.3. It was discovered in 1863 by the German chemists Ferdinand Reich and Hieronymus Richter. Indium is a rare element and occurs mainly in zinc minerals. Indium compounds have a deep indigo blue color in a flame. That is why the metal is called indium.

Indium is used to make alloys that have low melting points. These alloys are used in soldering and in fire alarm systems. It is also used in electronic components such as transistors and in making mirrors. M.E./J.R.W.

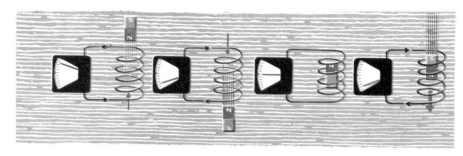

Electromagnetic induction is shown at left. 1. Moving a magnet through a coil induces a current in the coil. 2. Moving the magnet the other way reverses the current. 3. If the magnet stops moving, the voltage is zero. 4. If the magnet moves faster, it induces a higher voltage.

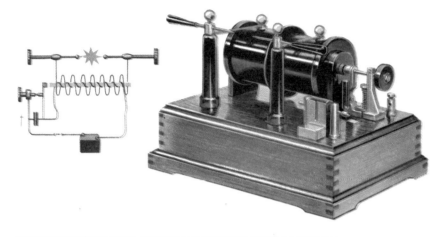

An induction coil and circuit diagram (far left) are shown. Low voltage current passing through the primary (inside) coil is rapidly switched on and off, alternatively magnetizing and demagnetizing the iron core. This induces a high voltage "kick" in the secondary (outside) coil, causing a spark to jump across the spark gap. A transformer is shown at left.

INDUCTION (in dək′ shən) Electromagnetic induction was first discovered by an English scientist, Michael Faraday. (*See* FARADAY, MICHAEL.) He placed some wire between the poles of a magnet. Then he joined the ends of the wire through an instrument that could detect an electric current. When the wire was moved through the magnetic field, a current flowed through it. This is called electromagnetic induction.

Faraday also discovered a similar effect. He placed two coils of wire near to each other. Then he passed an alternating current through one of the coils. An alternating current is continually changing and reverses its flow at short intervals. Because the current is changing, it sets up a magnetic field around itself. This field changes with the current. Faraday found that a similar current is induced in the second coil. It is induced by the changing magnetic field.

This effect is used in transformers. (*See* TRANSFORMER.) They are used to change high voltages to low ones, and vice versa. In a transformer, the voltage in one coil is used to induce a voltage in the other. The size of the induced voltage depends on the number of turns of wire in each coil. *See also* ELECTROMAGNETISM.   M.E./J.T.

INDUCTION (LOGICAL) Induction (in dək′ shən) is a method of investigation used by scientists. When scientists perform experiments, they make observations. They then try to explain the results of their observations in a theory. Then they, or other scientists, perform more experiments to test the theory. This method of investigating the world is called induction. It is the opposite of deduction. In deduction, you start with a theory. Then you perform experiments to confirm that the theory is accurate. *See also* SCIENCE.   M.E./A.I.

INERTIA (in ər′ shə) Inertia is the tendency of matter to remain at rest unless acted upon by an outside force. Inertia is also the tendency of a moving body to continue moving in the same direction. The greater the mass of the matter, the greater its inertia. For example, an automobile has greater inertia than a bicycle. It takes less effort to get the bicycle moving than it does to get the automobile moving. A person sitting in a moving automobile that stops suddenly still keeps moving forward unless stopped by a safety belt.

W.R.P./J.T.

INERTIAL GUIDANCE (in ər′ shəl gīd′ əns) Inertial guidance is a system of navigating that does not depend upon observations of stars, planets, or the sun. Its function depends only on measurements of amount and direction of accelerations, or changes in velocity. It is used mainly in nuclear submarines, missiles, rockets, and transoceanic air transport planes.

Nuclear submarines are able to remain submerged for many months without surfacing. By remaining submerged, they reduce the risk of detection. However, they are not able to navigate by conventional methods. A special computer in the inertial guidance system records every change in the ship's speed and direction, the speed of currents under the ocean, and other factors. The computer can determine instantly the exact location of the submarine. Direction-sensing instruments that contain gyroscopes and speed-detecting devices, called accelerometers, feed information to the computer.

Most missiles and rockets employ a modified version of the submarine inertial guidance system. This system keeps the missile, or rocket, on a pre-selected course, and automatically makes corrections when it wanders from the desired path.   W.R.P./J.vP.

INFECTION (in fek′ shən) Infection is the invasion of the body by any germs causing disease, such as bacteria, viruses, or other microorganisms. The body has defenses against infection. The secretion of its glands helps to control bacteria. The skin forms a strong barrier. Most body openings, such as the ears, nose, and mouth, are lined with membranes that secrete sticky mucus to trap germs. Within the body there is a powerful system that attacks invading germs and neutralizes (makes harmless) their poisons. (*See* IMMUNITY.)

Germs can enter the body through breaks in the skin caused by injury or surgery. This is why cuts and burns must be kept clean. It is also why surgeons must make sure that their hands, clothes, and instruments are completely germ-free. (*See* ASEPSIS.) Biting insects spread a number of diseases by piercing the skin of their victims. Some germs can pass through the mucous membranes.

Many germs infect the body through the stomach and intestines. Such infection may result if a person consumes contaminated food or water. Many common germs are, however, destroyed by the acid in the stomach. The easiest route of all for many germs is by way of the lungs. A large number of common infectious diseases are spread by people breathing in tiny droplets of germ-filled moisture. These droplets are sprayed into the air whenever a person with an infectious disease coughs, sneezes, or simply exhales.

The use of antiseptics and other hygienic measures can reduce the chance of infection. (*See* HYGIENE.) But some diseases are so infectious that patients must be kept in isolation, or out of contact with other people except medical staff who are immune or specially protected.   J.J.A./J.J.F.

INFINITY (in fin′ ət ē) Infinity means an unlimited extent of space, time, or quantity. If you start counting the whole numbers from one, you will never reach the end. There is always a number bigger than any number that you can think of. The whole numbers are said to reach infinity. This simply means that they go on "forever." Infinity is sometimes represented by the symbol ∞.   M.E./S.P.A.

Facing left: the inflorescence of the hollyhock.

INFLAMMATION (in' flə mā' shən) Inflammation is a way in which the body reacts to injury or infection. The infected tissues become swollen, reddened, and warm. The inflamed area feels painful. The body temperature and pulse rate may both be increased. These changes are a result of the blood vessels in the area becoming dilated (enlarged), increasing the blood flow. The blood cells and blood vessels press on sensory nerves, causing pain. The walls of the capillaries, the smallest blood vessels, become more porous (filled with tiny holes). This allows white blood cells and other things in the blood to pass out to the affected tissues and to help to repair them or kill germs. J.J.A./J.J.F.

INFLORESCENCE (in' flə res' əns) An inflorescence is a cluster of flowers. Single flowers, such as the tulip, and flowers that grow at the bases of leaves, such as the morning glory, are not considered to be inflorescences. There are two basic types of inflorescence: determinate inflorescence and indeterminate inflorescence. In determinate inflorescence, the stem stops growing when a flower develops from a bud at the tip of the stem. (*See* HORMONE.) In determinate inflorescence, the stem continues growing as flowers develop near the tip. As the stem grows, more flowers are produced. As a result, the lower or inner flowers are older than the upper or outer ones. A.J.C./M.H.S.

INFLUENZA (in' flü en' zə) Influenza is a disease caused by several different virus strains. It is a very infectious disease. It spreads very rapidly from person to person. When a large number of people in the same area are affected, it is called an epidemic of influenza.

The influenza virus settles in the lining of the nose and throat. It causes sneezing, coughing, and sore throat. It can cause fever, sudden chills, and headache. Often the sufferer has aches and pains all over the body. He or she feels sick and completely exhausted. In most cases, influenza lasts between three days and a week.

Some kinds of influenza are very mild. Others are dangerous. The "Spanish flu" epidemic after World War I killed more people than were killed in the war itself. Fortunately there have been no more influenza epidemics as serious as that. However, because people can travel long distances very

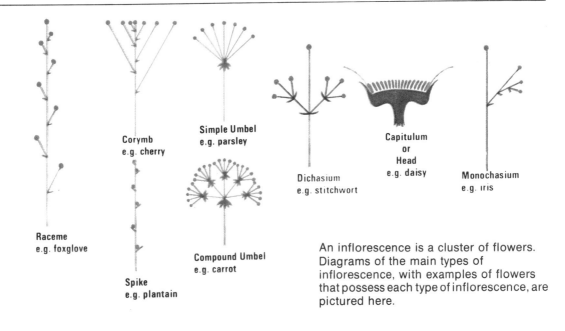

Raceme
e.g. foxglove

Corymb
e.g. cherry

Spike
e.g. plantain

Simple Umbel
e.g. parsley

Compound Umbel
e.g. carrot

Dichasium
e.g. stitchwort

Capitulum
or
Head
e.g. daisy

Monochasium
e.g. iris

An inflorescence is a cluster of flowers. Diagrams of the main types of inflorescence, with examples of flowers that possess each type of inflorescence, are pictured here.

rapidly today, epidemics may spread quickly around the world.

It is possible to prepare vaccines that give protection against virus diseases. But there are so many different strains of influenza that it is hard to prepare vaccines against them. If there seems to be a danger of an epidemic, then a vaccine against a particular kind of influenza can be prepared. The exact type of virus responsible is first identified. Millions of doses must be prepared to give the population immunity against the disease. (*See* IMMUNITY.)   D.M.H.W./J.J.F.

INFRARED RAY (in′ frə red′ rā′) An infrared ray is a beam of light that has a longer wavelength than visible light, and therefore cannot be seen by the human eye. Infrared rays are part of the electromagnetic spectrum. All objects give off infrared rays according to their temperature. The warmer an object is, the more infrared rays it gives off. During World War II, an instrument called a sniperscope was used to detect something warmer than its surroundings. This was valuable in finding enemies hiding in the dark or in fog. Infrared rays also have applications in photography and medical treatment. (*See* MEDICINE.) Astronomers make telescopic observations of infrared radiation to learn about planetary atmospheres and to measure stellar temperatures. Infrared rays were discovered by the British astronomer Sir William Herschel in 1800.   J.M.C./S.S.B.

INFRASONICS (in′ frə sän′ iks) Infrasonics is the study of vibrations, similar to sound waves, that have a very low frequency. Infrasonic waves are so low in frequency that they cannot be heard. They are below 20 hertz, which is the lowest frequency the human ear can hear. However, infrasonic waves can be felt, and, if the intensity, or strength, is high the vibrations can be damaging to the body tissue. *See also* FREQUENCY; SOUND.   W.R.P./J.T.

INGOT (ing′ gət) An ingot is a mass of metal cast into a size or shape convenient for storing, reshaping, or refining. For example, a gold ingot is often shaped like a bar. Steel ingots range in weight from a few grams or ounces to many tons. In addition to gold and steel, silver and tin are often cast into ingots.   J.M.C./R.W.L.

INJECTION (in jek′ shən) In medicine, many drugs or other fluids are forced into an opening, passage, or tissue in the body. The fluid enters the body through a hollow needle

This infrared photograph of the Rio Grande river was taken from a mile above the Texas-Mexico border. The pale blue of the river (left, above silvery patch of reflected sunlight) shows the presence of silt caused by pollution. The contrasting tones of the owbow lake (top center) and the lagoon (upper right) are the result of variations in the amount of infrared light reflected—again suggesting water pollution by different substances.

that penetrates the skin. This process is called injection. Injection may be performed in a number of ways with needles or "guns."

The equipment needed to perform a hypodermic injection includes a syringe and a hollow needle. A syringe is a tube attached to a plunger. The needle has a very sharp point. It slips easily into the skin. The doctor attaches the needle to the syringe barrel. He puts the liquid medicine in the syringe and places the needle into the patient's skin. The doctor then presses on the plunger. This forces the medicine through the needle. There are different types of hypodermic injections. They are named for the tissue into which the injection is made. Intradermal injections are made between the layers of skin. Injections made below the layers of skin are called subcutaneous injections. In an intramuscular injection, the needle penetrates a muscle.

A hypodermic needle can be used to give an intravenous injection. An intravenous injection is one given inside a vein. Doctors use intravenous injections to put needed substances into the bloodstream. When blood, blood plasma, or serum is given this way, it is called a transfusion. Patients who cannot eat or drink are kept alive by intravenous feeding of water containing sugar, amino acids, vitamins, and minerals. *See also* BLOOD TRANSFUSION. J.J.A./J.J.F.

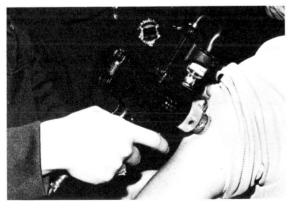

Modern injections are administered with a gun, rather than a hypodermic needle.

INORGANIC CHEMISTRY (in' ȯr' gan' ik kem' ə strē) Chemistry is the study of elements and compounds. Compounds are formed when different elements combine with each other. Compounds are divided into two groups: organic compounds and inorganic compounds. Inorganic chemistry studies the chemical properties of inorganic compounds. It also studies the chemical properties of the elements themselves. Roughly speaking, inorganic compounds do not contain carbon. However a few carbon compounds are counted as inorganic, such as the gas carbon dioxide. People used to think that organic compounds only occurred in living, or organic, matter. Inorganic compounds were thought to be found only in minerals and nonliving, or inorganic, matter. But this is now known to be not strictly true. M.E./A.D.

INSECT

An insect (in' sekt) is any of more than one million species of invertebrate animals belonging to the class Insecta of the phylum Arthropoda. (*see* ARTHROPODA.) Insects live almost everywhere in the world except in the deep seas. They are the most widespread and successful animals that ever lived. Fossils indicate that insects existed more than 400 million years ago. Since that time, they have consistently been able to adapt quickly and efficiently to changes in the climate and environment. (*See* ADAPTATION.)

Insect body The body of an insect is divided into three sections: head, thorax, and abdomen. The head has one pair of antennae that is used for the senses of touch, taste, and smell. There are usually two compound eyes which provide good vision, and two or three simple eyes (ocelli) which detect light or darkness. (*See* EYE AND VISION.) The mouth may have biting or chewing jaws, or may have piercing and sucking structures. The mouths of some insects have unmovable jaws with spongelike pads for absorbing liquids. The head also contains a brain which connects with nerve cords in all parts of the body.

The thorax, or middle part of the body, has three pairs of jointed legs. These legs are equipped with sticky pads or claws at the ends. Insects are the only invertebrates with wings. Although most insects have two pairs of wings, some have only one pair, or no wings at all. Some of the wingless insects have small knobs where the wings would normally be. (*See* VESTIGIAL ORGAN.) Other wingless insects may have lost the wings during evolution or may never have had wings at any point in their history. (*See* EVOLUTION.)

The abdomen, or end part of the body, contains organs for digestion, excretion, respiration, and reproduction. There are tiny

openings along the length of the abdomen called spiracles. These spiracles open to the tracheae, or air tubes, through which an insect breathes. Oxygen diffuses into the blood from the tracheae at a fairly slow rate. (*See* DIFFUSION.) This is probably a major reason that insects have stayed small throughout evolution. The abdomen also contains malpighian tubules. (*See* EXCRETION.) These tubules remove wastes from the blood while recycling most of the water to the body. For this reason, insects can live for long periods of time without water. A female insect often has an egg-laying tube called an ovipositor. In some insects, the ovipositor has been modified for use as a stinger.

An insect's body is covered with a tough exoskeleton. (*See* SKELETON.) This exoskeleton is lighter and stronger than bone. It provides protection from injury and loss of moisture, and serves as a place of attachment for muscles. Since the exoskeleton does not in-

The goliath beetle (below) of Africa is the world's largest insect. It is about the size of an adult person's fist. Insects live almost everywhere in the world except in the deep seas. Insects existed more than 400 million years ago.

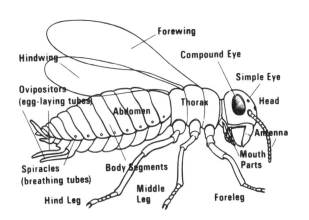

The body of a typical adult insect (left) is divided into head, thorax, and abdomen, and covered with hard, horny chitin. Most insects have wings, and all have three pairs of legs. The head includes the brain, simple and compound eyes, antennae and mouth parts. Legs and wings are attached to the thorax. The abdomen contains the digestive, excretory, and reproductive organs.

Insects (below) are divided into three broad groups according to the extent of metamorphosis they undergo during their development into adults. The three groups are complete, incomplete, and gradual metamorphosis.

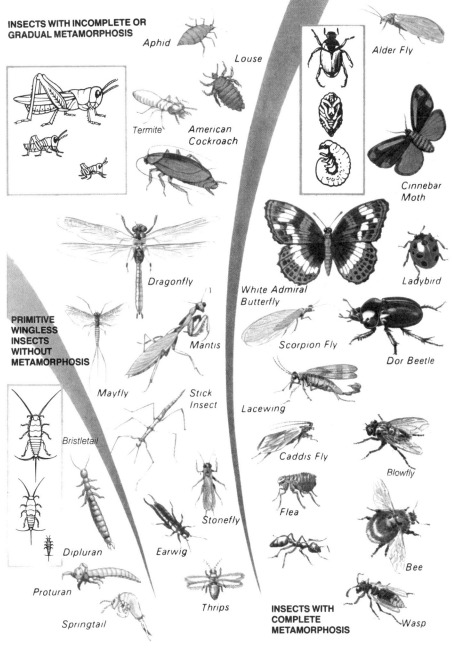

INSECTS WITH INCOMPLETE OR GRADUAL METAMORPHOSIS

Aphid

Louse

Termite

American Cockroach

Alder Fly

Cinnebar Moth

Dragonfly

White Admiral Butterfly

Ladybird

PRIMITIVE WINGLESS INSECTS WITHOUT METAMORPHOSIS

Mantis

Scorpion Fly

Dor Beetle

Mayfly

Stick Insect

Lacewing

Bristletail

Caddis Fly

Blowfly

Flea

Stonefly

Dipluran

Earwig

Proturan

Thrips

INSECTS WITH COMPLETE METAMORPHOSIS

Bee

Wasp

Springtail

crease in size as the insect grows larger, it must be shed several times during an insect's development. (*See* MOLTING.)

The entire body of an insect is usually covered with tiny bristles. These bristles are connected to nerves and are very sensitive to contact. It is for this reason that an insect can detect even the faintest breeze or movement.

Many insects have special hearing organs located on the abdomen, thorax, or legs. Some of these organs are spaces covered by a thin membrane which responds to vibrations in the air.

Insect life   One reason for the amazing success of insects is that they are able to reproduce quickly and in large numbers. Reproduction is usually sexual, the male inserting sperm into the female's body. As the female lays her eggs, they are fertilized by the sperm. (*See* FERTILIZATION.) The fertilized eggs are usually not tended by the insect, but develop near or in a source of nourishment and protection. In some cases, fertilization is external. This means that the female lays the eggs and then the male fertilizes them. Some insects produce eggs which develop into adults without being fertilized. (*See* PARTHE-NOGENESIS.)

As an insect develops, it goes through several changes before becoming an adult. Some primitive insects develop directly from the eggs. Most, however, go through several stages of development called metamorphosis. (*See* MEATMORPHOSIS.) In complete metamorphosis, there are four stages of development: egg, larva, pupa, adult. In incomplete metamorphosis, there are three stages: egg, nymph, adult. The nymph is like a small adult. As the insect goes through its development, it molts several times. The entire process of metamorphosis may take a few days or several years, depending on species and environmental conditions. Many insects lay eggs which can survive the winter or other unfavorable conditions. (*See* DORMANCY.)

Insects and human beings   Although many people think of insects as bothersome pests, most insects perform many important services. Harmful insects, however, cause billions of dollars of losses every year to crops and plants. Some insects bite or sting animals and human beings. Some of these biting insects carry disease-causing microorganisms such as bacteria, fungi, viruses, and wormlike parasites. (*See* DISEASE; MICRO-ORGANISM.)

Many insects, however, are of vital importance to human beings. They are responsible for most of the pollination of plants. (*See* POLLINATION.) Some insects eat or live off of weeds or other, more harmful insects. Some insects make tunnels in the ground which help aerate the soil. Insects are the major source of food for birds, fish, and many other animals. In some countries, insects are used as food for human beings. Some insects feed on dead and decaying material, and form a vital link in the food chain. (*See* FOOD CHAIN.) Insects also provide silk, honey, and wax. Insects themselves are used as a source of substances used in dyes, shellacs, medicines, and many other products.

Insect control   Harmful insects are often controlled by chemicals called insecticides. (*See* INSECTICIDE.) Because of the ability of insects to adapt quickly to negative environmental conditions (such as being sprayed with insecticides), they soon become resistant to these chemicals. As a result, entomologists and other biologists are constantly experimenting with new, safer means of control. They have developed methods of introducing predators, parasites, and insect diseases to control insects. (*See* BIOLOGICAL CONTROL.) Recently, sterilized males have been used as a method of control. Large numbers of these males are released in areas where control is desired. They mate with the females which then lay unfertilized eggs. These eggs fail to develop. Since many harmful insects thrive in organic wastes, they can often be controlled by improving sanitary conditions. *See also* ENTOMOLOGY; PROTECTIVE COLORATION; WARNING COLORATION.   A.J.C./J.E.R.

INSECTICIDE (in sek′ tə sīd′) An insecticide is a chemical pesticide used to kill harmful insects. The use of insecticides has helped save many crops and ornamental plants that would have been killed by insects. The discovery of a very powerful insecticide called DDT (chemical name DichloroDiphenyl-Trichloroethane) was a major factor in winning battles in the South Pacific during World War II. The DDT was sprayed over islands where malaria-carrying mosquitoes lived. The malaria disease had killed and weakened many soldiers, but the soldiers were able to stay healthy after they killed the mosquitoes with DDT. (*See* MALARIA; MOSQUITO.)

There are some insecticides which are simple compounds found in nature. Most, however, are complex chemicals made by man. They kill insects in one of two ways. Some will kill the insect if it is sprayed on the body of the insect. Other insecticides have to be eaten in order to work. These are sprayed on leaves which insects eat.

Insecticides have caused problems, too. Many are poisonous to valuable animals such as birds and fish. When a large forest is sprayed with an insecticide, much of it will be washed by rains into the streams in the forest. In this way, fish can become poisoned. Often, animals such as worms will be sprayed by an insecticide. This will not kill the worm, but when a bird, such as a robin, eats several of these worms, it may die. Scientists have found that some birds of prey, such as ospreys and falcons, can survive with large amounts of insecticides in their bodies. However, this causes the shells of their eggs to be very thin and easy to break. Most eggs then break and few young birds are hatched. Because of this, ospreys and falcons are becoming very rare.

Another problem with many insecticides, such as DDT, is that they do not go away. When DDT is washed into a stream, it may stay in the mud or water for ten years. Because of this, many insecticides are no longer used in many countries.

In recent years, some insects—especially mosquitoes—have become immune to insecticides. The chemicals no longer kill them. (*See* IMMUNITY.) Scientists now understand why this happens. There are always a few mosquitoes that are not affected by a chemical. There may be only 2 out of 10,000 mosquitoes which survive a spraying of DDT. These two mosquitoes reproduce and their offspring inherit the immunity to DDT. (*See* GENETICS.) Soon there are 1,000 mosquitoes that are immune to DDT. In a few years, there are 10,000 mosquitoes again, but they are all immune to DDT. Scientists must keep developing new insecticides to kill these insects. *See also* AGRICULTURE; CONSERVATION, ECOLOGY.   S.R.G./R.J.B.

An insecticide comes from the pyrethrum flower.

INSECTIVORE (in sek′ tə vōr′) An insectivore is an organism that eats insects. Most insectivores are animals, but there are insectivorous plants such as the Venus's-flytrap. Insects that land or crawl onto a special leaf of the plant are trapped and digested. Insectivorous animals include shrews, moles, bats, and other mammals. Some of them eat nothing but insects, but others also eat small animals such as worms. Insectivores usually have sharp teeth in order to kill and chew the insects, which sometimes have tough shells. *See also* CARNIVORE; HERBIVORE; OMNIVORE; VENUS'S-FLYTRAP. S.R.G./R.J.B.

The common shrew (above) is a typical insectivore. Insectivores are organisms that eat insects.

INSOLATION (in′ sō lā′ shen) Insolation is the heat and light energy that the earth and other planets of the solar system receive from the sun. The word "insolation" comes from the three words "incoming solar radiation."

On earth, the greatest insolation is at the equator. The least insolation is at the North and South Poles. The amount of insolation depends upon the angle of the sun's rays. There is more insolation where the rays fall more directly. More solar radiation is received during the spring and summer than in the fall and winter. Insolation is not as great when the skies are cloudy or when there is a high pollution level in the atmosphere. *See also* CLIMATE; SEASON. J.M.C./C.R.

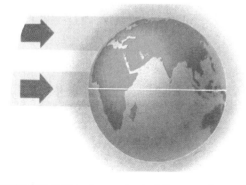

The earth's insolation is greatest at the equator and least at high altitudes.

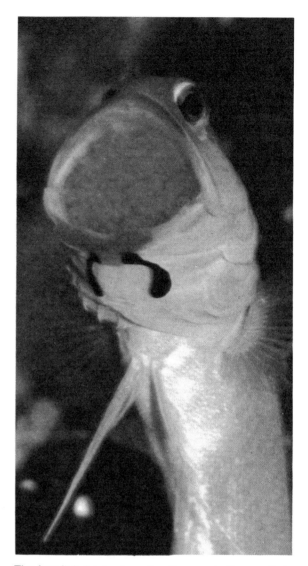

The jaw fish (above) carries its eggs in its mouth to protect them—an example of parental instinct.

INSTINCT (in′ stingkt) Instinct is behavior that animals demonstrate that they have neither learned nor experienced. Instincts are behavior patterns that are inborn. The behavior is inherited, passed from one generation to the next.

For a behavior to be considered instinctive, it must be something that is demonstrated by all of the males, or all of the females, or all of both sexes of a species. Examples of instinctive behavior are the maternal behavior of a mother toward her young, the reverse response in which the young follow their

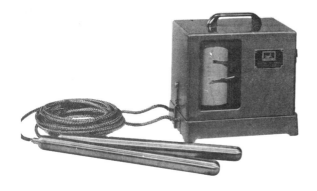

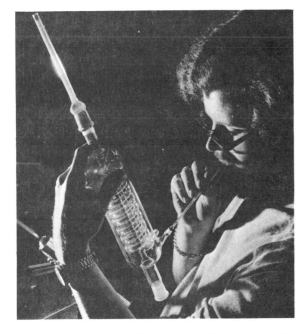

A thermograph (top left) records continuous temperature measurements. Traditional skills (bottom left) are used in making this glass condenser. An electron microscope (above) provides more powerful magnifications than optical microscopes.

mother, the courtship behavior between male and female, and migration from one location to another.

Instinctive behavior begins with a special stimulus, something that makes the animal act as it does. The stimulus might be a specific color or a particular movement. A certain change in the environment can also serve as a stimulus to some species. Whatever the stimulus, it can cause hormones to be released that in turn make the animal carry out its instinctive behavior. *See also* BEHAVIOR OF ANIMALS; PSYCHOLOGY.   J.J.A./R.J.B.

INSTRUMENT, SCIENTIFIC A scientific instrument (in′ strə mənt) is a tool that people use to gather knowledge about the world around them. Everything that people know about their surroundings comes through their senses, such as sight, hearing, and smell. However, peoples' senses have limitations. That is where scientific instruments come into use. Some things are too small to see with the unaided eye. Other things are too far away. Some sounds are beyond the range of a person's hearing. Such things as electricity and atomic radiation can only be detected or measured by instruments.

People's senses do not provide precise enough information under all conditions. For example, our eyes can easily compare the brightness of two electric lights. But they are less effective at judging how bright one lighted room is compared to another. Sometimes, peoples' senses give misleading information. If you place one hand in cold water, and the other hand in hot water, both hands soon feel neither hot nor cold. If you then put both hands in lukewarm water, the hand that was in the hot water feels cool, and the other hand feels warm. Thermometers give you a much more accurate measurement of temperature than your hands.

Most scientific instruments have three things in common: (1) a transducer, (2) a scale of values, and (3) a readout. The transducer tells the quantity being measured. The scale of values provides a comparison with the output of the transducer. The readout gives the result of the instrument reading. A thermometer, for example, uses a glass tube containing mercury as a transducer. The numbers along the tube are the scale of values. The position of the mercury along the numbers provides the readout that tells what the temperature is.

There are two main types of scientific instruments—graphic instruments and measuring instruments. Graphic instruments present an entire picture at once so that one part of the picture can be compared to other parts. Cameras, microscopes, and telescopes are the best-known graphic instruments. Others include spectroscopes, oscilloscopes, and nuclear particle detectors. (*See* ACCELERATOR, PARTICLE.)

Measuring instruments tell the number of measurement units involved in whatever they are measuring. A measuring stick tells the length of a table in meters and centimeters, or feet and inches. A micrometer can measure the thickness of such materials as paper, or thin metal foil. The laser rangefinder can measure the distance from the earth to the moon within centimeters.

Accurate measurement plays such an important part in science that some people believe science is basically measurement. Quantities most often measured include length, temperature, electric current, time, and weight. Most other measured quantities are related to these basic ones. Each kind of quantity requires a certain kind of measuring instrument to measure it. Many types of thermometers measure temperature. Balances and scales measure weight. Clocks measure time. Several types of instruments, including ammeters and voltmeters, measure electricity. W.R.P./R.W.L.

INSULATION (in′ sə lā′ shən) Insulation is material that protects against heat, cold, electricity, or sound. Clothing is one of the most common types of insulation. Wool clothes are warmer than those made of most other fabrics. Air becomes trapped in the meshes of the wool fiber. This dead (motionless) air does not conduct heat easily, and serves as a protective layer between the body and the outside air. This prevents body heat from escaping. Other kinds of insulation do not readily permit electricity or sound to pass through. These include the rubber or other coating that surrounds electrical wires, and the soundproofing found in theaters and homes.

Many materials provide protection against heat and cold. The body is protected by clothing made of various textiles. Generally, several layers of light clothing provide greater protection than one thick layer with the same total weight. This is due to the insulating effect of the air between the layers. The same principle is applied to insulation in homes and other structures. For example, the layer of air between storm windows and the regular windows provides insulation.

Home insulation is extremely important for comfortable and economical living. The loss of heat in uninsulated houses is so high that insulation in the outside walls and top ceilings pays for itself in lower fuel bills. The hollow spaces in walls and ceilings are usually filled with insulation. Several types of insulation are used for houses, including (1) batt, (2) blanket, (3) loose-fill, (4) rigid, and (5) reflective insulation.

Batt insulation is made in soft, flexible units that fit between rafters and joists. Batts are made of fireproof, fibrous material, such as treated wood fiber, hair felt, flax fiber, eel grass, or shredded paper. This material is stitched between two layers of waterproof paper. Batts are available in thicknesses up to 15 cm [6 in]. The fill material in batts may also be made of mineral wool, an insulating material made from the slag (mineral refuse) recovered from iron-making blast furnaces.

Blanket insulation is similar to batt insulation, but it comes in long rolls instead of pieces. A roll usually contains about 9 square meters [100 sq ft]. Loose-fill insulation comes in bulk form, in bags, or bales. Mineral wool in the form of pellets, expanded mica, granulated cork, and other materials are types of loose-fill insulation. Loose-fill insulation is poured or blown into place.

Rigid insulation consists of thick sheets of fiberboard. It is usually nailed to the outside walls, and then covered with wood siding or bricks. Reflective insulation consists of thin copper or aluminum sheets, or of copper or aluminum foil. It is often applied to the surfaces of rigid insulation, plasterboard, or even heavy paper. The metallic surfaces of these materials reflect heat waves.

Other kinds of heat and cold insulation include asbestos and cork. Both materials are expensive and have specialized uses. Asbestos is used to insulate furnaces and hot pipes. Cork is used in refrigeration.

Refractory materials are used to insulate against high temperatures in industrial furnaces, boilers, and incinerators. Refractories are made of non-metallic substances such as quartzite, sandstone, fire clay, bauxite, and graphite. They withstand temperatures of up to 2,000°C [3,632°F], well over the melting point of iron. Refractories also resist thermal shock (sudden large changes in temperature), and chemical actions of gases and liquids.

Soundproofing is a type of insulation. There are two different types. One type consists of sound-absorbing or sound-deadening, materials placed on walls and ceilings to reduce echoes. These materials make a speaker's voice more distinct. They also improve the quality of music by reducing objectionable echoes. Materials used for this purpose are perforated cardboard, fiberboard, corkboard, hair felt covered with burlap, and special types of acoustical tiles and plaster. These materials reduce echoes because they contain many air passages that take excess energy away from sound waves.

Another type of soundproofing reduces the sound transferred from room to room by vibration of the walls and floors. Sound waves make these surfaces vibrate. This causes air in contact with these surfaces to vibrate and cause other sounds. This type of sound transmission is difficult to overcome. However, building materials such as concrete, brick, and stone are used because they produce less vibration than wood and fiberboard. Floor coverings, such as carpets, heavy linoleum, rubber tiles, and cork tiles help insulate against floor vibrations. (*See* ACOUSTICS.)

Electrical insulation is made from materials that do not conduct electricity. These include rubber, glass, cotton, paraffin, certain plastics, and other materials.   W.R.P./J.T.

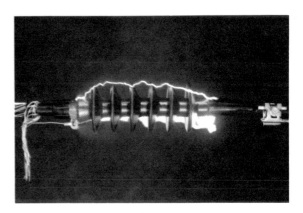

A terminal insulator (above) is being tested for a 15,000 volt power cable. Flashover for this insulator happens at over 165,000 volts—more than 10 times the voltage the insulator is supposed to absorb during normal use.

INSULIN (in' sə lən) Insulin is a hormone formed in the body by a gland called the pancreas, which is located near the stomach.

(*See* HORMONE.) Like other hormones, insulin is used to regulate another organ of the body. Insulin acts to help the body use sugar and starches.

The pancreas does two important jobs. It produces juices called enzymes, which help the digestion of food in the intestine. In addition, about a million cells of the pancreas form tiny islands named the islets of Langerhans. These cells make insulin, which gets it name from *insula*, the Latin word for island.

After a person eats, sugar and starches are converted into glucose and go into the blood stream. Insulin is also released into the blood stream to help the body to use the glucose for energy. The body also uses glucose to make protein for healthy muscles.

Insulin is the "spark" to help burn the glucose. In a healthy person, the body produces enough insulin to utilize what he has eaten. Without enough insulin, the body cannot use up the food, and sugar builds up in the blood stream. This condition is called sugar diabetes. The medical term for it is diabetes mellitus. A person who has the condition is called a diabetic.

Before 1921, a person who had diabetes usually did not live very long. But in 1921, two Canadians, physician Dr. Frederick Banting and medical student Charles Best,

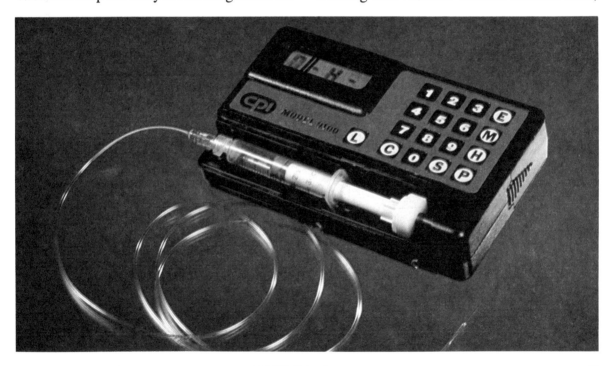

Shown above is an Ambulatory Insulin Infusion Pump. It is a computerized device that is programmed to inject precise amounts of insulin. A diabetes patient may wear the pump under a shirt or blouse or on a belt around the waist.

were able to isolate the insulin-producing cells from the pancreas of animals. They were awarded the Nobel Prize in Medicine and Physiology in 1923 for their work.

Insulin taken from the glands of pork and beef animals is used to keep alive millions of people who suffer from diabetes. The insulin cells are extracted, purified, and mixed into various combinations to meet the specific needs of the many types of diabetics. In 1981, using the discoveries of genetic engineering, biologists found a way to use bacteria to produce insulin. (*See* GENETICS.)

Because it is a protein, insulin must be injected into the body. It cannot be taken orally because it would be absorbed without providing the ''spark'' to help burn glucose.

The pancreas of a healthy person automatically releases enough insulin. The diabetic does not receive insulin on demand from his own pancreas. His one or two daily insulin injections must be balanced by his food intake. Insulin, timing, food, and exercise must be carefully controlled so that the diabetic can lead a normal life.

Insulin to be taken by injection is available in various strengths. It can also be made to act as quickly as necessary. Shots are a lifetime routine, and the diabetic usually learns to give the shots to himself. To keep any part of the body from developing scar tissue or becoming uncomfortable, the locations where the injection is given must be rotated. Usually shots are given on the thighs, abdomen, upper arms, and buttocks.

Today it is possible for some diabetic patients to be cured with a pancreas transplant. In transplant surgery, the healthy pancreas of a person who has died is used to replace the diseased pancreas of the diabetic.

An artificial pancreas, which is like a small pump implanted in the patient's body, can also be used to treat diabetes. By automatically releasing insulin in tiny amounts throughout the day, the artificial pancreas eliminates the need for injections.   V.A./G.B.

INTEGRATED CIRCUIT An integrated circuit (int′ə grāt′əd sər′ ket), or IC, consists of various components and their connections, all of which are produced on a small piece, or wafer, of silicon. The silicon is a semiconducting material that is neither a good conductor nor a nonconductor. (*See* SEMICONDUCTOR.) It replaces the wires used previously to connect components in ordinary electronic circuits. The IC can also be called a monolithic integrated circuit. It is a solid state device which controls a signal flowing in certain solid materials like semiconducting silicon. Different amounts of impurities are added to various parts of the silicon to make these parts act like individual electronic components, such as transistors, resistors, diodes, and capacitors.

The first integrated circuits were built in the 1960s. They were used in military equipment and spacecraft, and helped make possible the first manned space flights. ICs were later used in personal radios, TV sets, computers, and other electronic devices. Development of microprocessors, or chips, that use ICs led to their widespread use in producing smaller, more economical electronic devices in the early 1970s. (*See* CHIP.) New electronic devices include pocket-sized calculators and computers, digital watches, video games, various home appliances, and controls to operate some types of industrial machines. (*See* CALCULATOR; COMPUTER; MICROCOMPUTER.)

Producing an integrated circuit first involves making a large drawing—a layout of the circuit. The layout drawing is reduced photographically to produce a set of masks. The masks provide the pattern for engraving the actual circuit. Next, wafers of silicon, which may be about three inches in diameter, are placed in a furnace where they are heated to form an oxide layer on their surfaces. Then they are coated with an emulsion that is sensitive to light. The masks are placed over the emulsion and a light is shone on them to expose the emulsion to the pattern. Exposed

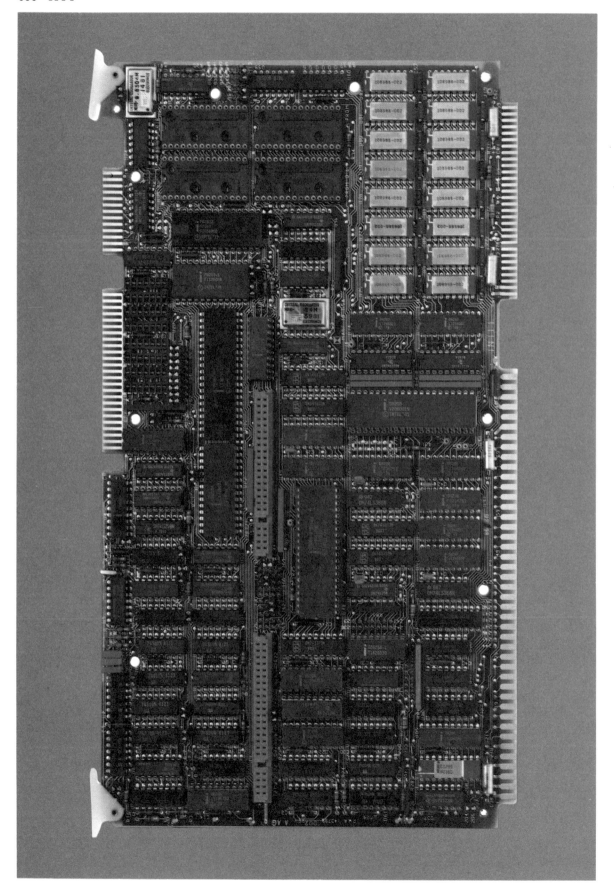

This integrated-circuit board is about 18 by 30 cm [7 by 12 in]. It contains the electronic elements for an entire computer system.

areas are then hardened, and the wafers are etched with acid. The acid dissolves the oxide areas not protected by a coating of hardened emulsion. Using the latest technology VLSI (very-large-scale integration), hundreds of thousands of circuits can be etched into a single wafer. After the ICs have been built into the silicon wafers, each one is tested on an automatic machine which scans the circuits with contact probes to test their electronic functions. The wafers are mounted on ceramic bases that contain connecting leads. The connecting leads are bonded to the circuit after it has been mounted on its ceramic base. The IC is then ready to be placed in a protective plastic casing.

Integrated circuits have many advantages over standard electronic circuits. They are much smaller, lighter, and they operate faster. They use much less power, cost less, and last longer. ICs also make repairing electronic devices easier, since the entire circuit is simply replaced instead of having to find individual faulty parts.

Microprocessor technology using ICs has resulted in microcomputers. Computers can now be made small enough to be held in a hand. Manufacturers of computers and other electronic devices use ICs to reduce both the size and cost of new equipment. ICs are very small. They can be a thousandth of a centimeter [0.0004 in] thick and a tenth of a centimeter [0.04 in] across.   S.K.L./G.D.B.

INTELLIGENCE (in tel′ ə jəns) Most scientists define intelligence as the ability to learn or understand. People differ in the speed in which they learn things. They differ in their ability to understand ideas. They differ in how well and how long they remember ideas. They also differ in how they use their knowledge and memory of situations in the past to solve problems. There is no fully ac-

cepted definition of intelligence. But intelligence involves the abilities mentioned above.

Such abilities are not separate things. They are all related. However, a person may do well in one thing and poorly in another. A person may find it very easy to memorize names and dates. But that person may find it difficult to do long division. Someone may have great creative talent in art or music, but can't remember where he or she left an object. Although creativity and intelligence are related, some people of above-average intelligence do poorly when faced with problems totally new to them.

Many psychologists believe that intelligence can be measured with various kinds of tests. The intelligence tests serve as an indication of how well a person will do when facing specific problems in everyday life. Psychologists figure the results of an intelligence test and assign it a number called an IQ. IQ stands for intelligence quotient. To determine an IQ, tests are given to find a person's mental age. The mental age is found by comparing test results with what is expected of people the same age. An 8-year-old and a 16-year-old may both have the mental age of 12. The mental age of the younger child is far above the chronological age (age in years). The older child's mental age is far below his or her chronological age. Psychologists have developed a formula for comparison purposes:

$$IQ = \frac{MA \text{ (mental age)}}{CA \text{ (chronological age)}} \times 100$$

First the mental age is divided by the chronological age. When the quotient is multiplied by 100, the resulting number is the IQ. This number is used to show how someone's intelligence compares with that of other people of the same chronological age. In the example above, the 8-year-old child's IQ is 150—above the average of 100. The 16-year-old child's is 75—below average.

Chimpanzees and humans are the two most intelligent animals. Facing left: a human infant and a chimpanzee infant. The chimpanzee and the human develop physical alertness and communication skills at different speeds.

Many people believe that intelligence tests do not really measure intelligence. Many tests seem to measure what someone has learned. They do not measure how quickly or slowly a person can learn. Therefore, these tests do not give a complete picture of the many factors that make up intelligence.

There is no absolute answer to where intelligence comes from. Scientists are still trying to find out what makes one person intelligent and another not so intelligent. But it can be said that peoples' intelligence depends on their heredity and their environment. Every person is born with a certain mental ability. The development of that ability may be activated or slowed down by his or her background. A child whose family speaks several languages, but depends on outside help for simple mechanical repairs, will probably find learning a new language easier than learning how an automobile engine works. A child who suffered from a very poor diet in infancy may not be able to develop his or her natural abilities. In a similar way, a child who was constantly ridiculed or beaten may become so upset that he or she may not be able to develop intellectual abilities. Many children who face discrimination because of race or physical defects fail to develop their mental abilities.

Generally, intelligence seems to be a result of both heredity and upbringing. Scientists have long disagreed about which is the more important. They will probably continue to do so for a long time. Despite major findings and advances in all fields of science, much about the human mind remains a mystery. *See also* BINET, ALFRED.   J.J.A./J.J.F.

INTENSITY (in ten′ sət ē) Intensity is the measure of the strength of radiant energy, such as light, magnetism, and sound.

Light intensity is the energy in watts sent out from a source over a given area. The area is usually a ''solid angle'' of a sphere called a steradian. (*See* LIGHT; PHOTOMETRY.)

The intensity of a magnetic field is measured in units of gauss. The intensity of the Earth's magnetic field is about 0.5 gauss. A magnetometer is the instrument used to measure the strength of a magnetic field. (*See* MAGNETISM.)

Sound intensity is measured in watts per square centimeter. When measuring the difference in intensity of two sounds, a unit called the bel is used. Each bel means an increase or decrease of 10 times the intensity. Therefore, if a fire engine siren has an intensity of ten times greater than the intensity of a buzzer, the siren has an intensity 1 bel greater than the buzzer. The decibel (1/10 of a bel) is the more common unit for measuring sound intensity. *See also* DECIBEL; SOUND.   J.M.C./J.T.

INTERFERENCE (int′ ə fir′ əns) All waves have crests (high points) and troughs (low points). A crest is where the disturbance is greatest in one direction. A trough is where the disturbance is greatest in the other direction. In a sea wave, for example, the highest point of the wave is the crest. The lowest point is the trough.

Interference is when two waves combine to reinforce or cancel each other out. The two waves must have about the same wavelength to interfere. The wavelength is the distance between one crest and the next. The waves must also be coherent. This means that the crests and troughs of different parts of the wave must coincide.

Interference can occur with any kind of wave, such as sound waves, water waves, light and radio waves. An easy way to produce interference is to pass a lightwave through two holes. This splits the wave up. After the two parts pass through the holes, they recombine and interfere. In some places, the crests of the two waves coincide. At these points, the light is strongest. This is called constructive interference. In other places, the crest of one wave coincides with the trough of the other. This is called destructive interference. The two waves cancel each other out. If light is used, then a series of light and dark bands are produced. This is called an interference pattern.

Interference can also occur between radio waves. The aerial of a radio receiver may pick up an unwanted signal. This signal can interfere with the main signal being picked up by the aerial. The interference produces a background crackling or hiss. Lightning causes interference with radio signals, as do some electric motors. A radio station sometimes broadcasts on a frequency close to that of another station. (*See* FREQUENCY.) These two signals can also interfere with one another.

M.E./A.I.

Two sets of water waves illustrate interference. If the crests of one set of waves meet the troughs of another, they cancel each other out and the waves disappear. If crests meet crests, they reinforce each other.

INTERFEROMETER (int′ ə fə räm′ ət ər) An interferometer is an instrument that produces interference of light. (*See* INTERFERENCE.) Albert Michelson, the American physicist, invented a very accurate interferometer about 1880. In the Michelson interferometer, a beam of light is split by a special mirror, which reflects some of the light, and the rest passes through. The two beams are then recombined by other mirrors. The beams travel different distances and so are out of step. Thus they interfere destructively. The

interference pattern can be viewed. Interferometers are used to measure the wavelength of light rays.

Interference can also be produced between two radio waves. This effect is used in radio astronomy. Two radio telescopes pick up signals from the same source. These two signals are then combined in an interferometer. Their interference pattern tells scientists more about the source than one signal would.

M.E./S.S.B.

INTERFERON (int′ ər fir′ än′) When viruses attack the body, it produces a substance called interferon. Interferon stops viruses from spreading and multiplying.

Viruses can multiply only by getting into a living cell. Viruses use the cell's own machinery to make new viruses. This usually kills the cell. The viruses then spread to nearby cells and repeat their work. Interferon is made whenever cells are attacked. In other words, the presence of a virus in a cell causes the cell to make interferon.

Interferon was discovered in 1957. It works only within a single species. For example, mouse interferon does not protect human beings. Human interferon does not help mice. Attempts to make interferon in a test tube have failed. But in 1970, scientists discovered that placing a form of nucleic acid made in the laboratory into animals causes their bodies to make interferon. When this is done, the creatures are much more able to fight off attack by viruses. Scientists are working to produce interferon in the laboratory, using genesplicing techniques. (*See* GENETICS.) Most scientists believe that the main use of interferon will be to prevent, rather than cure, disease. *See also* IMMUNITY.

J.J.A./J.J.F.

INTERNAL COMBUSTION ENGINE (in tərn′ əl kəm bəs′ chən en′ jən) In an internal combustion engine, fuel is burned inside a cylinder to give off energy. Combustion is another word for burning. The engines that drive most cars and trucks work by internal combustion. They include gasoline, diesel, and Wankel engines. (*See* ENGINE.) In an external combustion engine, fuel is burned outside the engine to give heat. Steam engines work by external combustion. (*See* STEAM ENGINE.)

The first internal combustion engine was made in about 1860. It was invented by Jean Joseph Etienne Lenoir, an engineer who lived in Belgium. It burned gas. After this, in 1876, came the engine invented by Count Nikolaus August Otto, an engineer in Germany. His was the first engine to work on a four-stroke cycle. This kind of engine is still used today.

The first gasoline-burning engines that worked well were made in 1885 by the automobile pioneers Karl Benz and Gottlieb Daimler. Twelve years later, another German engineer, Rudolf Diesel, invented the diesel engine. It burned oil as fuel. In both gasoline and diesel engines, fuel is burned inside a cylinder. But in a gasoline engine, a spark from a spark plug causes the burning. In a diesel engine, the fuel is burned by pressing air so tightly together that it heats up. This system is called compression ignition. *See also* GAS TURBINE; ENGINE.   D.M.H.W./J.T.

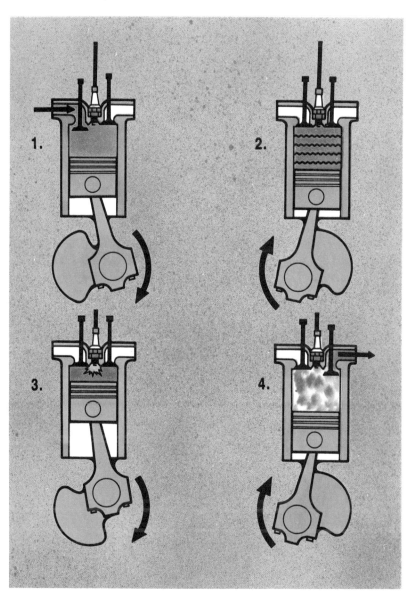

This illustration shows the four steps in the operation of a gasoline internal-combustion engine. (1) As the piston moves down, the intake valve opens and a mixture of gasoline and air enters the cylinder. (2) The intake valve closes, and the piston moves up, compressing the gasoline-air mixture. (3) When the piston reaches the top of the cylinder, the spark explodes the compressed gas, forcing the piston down. (4) The exhaust valve opens, and the piston moves up, pushing out the exploded gas. The piston next begins over at step 1. The continuous up-and-down motion of the piston turns the crankshaft, which turns the engine.

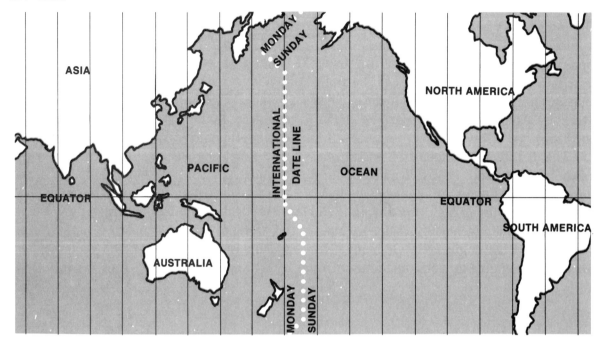

The international date line follows the line of 180° west, though it detours around islands.

INTERNATIONAL DATE LINE (int ər nash′ nəl dāt līn) The international date line is a line on a map that mostly follows another line called the 180° meridian. (*See* LATITUDE AND LONGITUDE.) It is found exactly halfway around the world from the Greenwich meridian (0°), which passes through Greenwich, England. (*See* PRIME MERIDIAN.) Everyone has agreed that the area east of the international date line is to be one day earlier than the area west of it.

If the international date line followed the 180° meridian for its total length, it would cross land areas. This would cause confusion about the date. So the date line runs around land areas. The eastern tip of Siberia has the same date as the rest of Asia. The Aleutian Islands have the same date as the rest of North America. The line also zigzags south of the equator so that New Zealand has the same date as Australia. *See also* TIME; TIME ZONE.

J.M.C./C.R.

INTERNATIONAL SYSTEM (int′ ər nash′ nəl sis′ təm) The International System of Units is a standardized system of weights and measures that is used throughout the world. It is also called the metric system. The United States and Canada, the last two countries to use the older English system (foot-pound-second system), are now slowly converting to the International, or metric system.

Units in the International System are usually referred to as SI units, from the French Système Internationale. The French system was created in 1790, and put into general use in that country in 1840.

As does any system of weights and measures, the International System defines quantities such as length and mass. Measuring in all parts of the world can be consistent with one another from using the same system of weights and measures.

The International System's units are derived from the meter-kilogram-second system of units. Some of the system's equivalents are:

1 meter (m) = 1.1 yards (yd)
1 kilometer (km) = 0.6 miles (mi)
1 liter (l) = 1.06 quarts (qt)
1 kilogram (kg) = 2.2 pounds (lb)
degrees Celsius (°C) =
    1.8 degrees Fahrenheit (°F) + 32

See also METRIC SYSTEM.   W.R.P./R.W.L.

INTESTINE (in tes' tən) The intestine is a long, folded, and looped tube that forms the largest part of the digestive system. It extends from the stomach to the anus. Together with the cavity of the mouth, the esophagus (gullet), and the stomach, it makes up the alimentary canal. The intestine is also called the bowel, or sometimes the gut. Inside it are carried out nearly all the processes of digestion. All of the food materials that the body absorbs pass through the walls of the intestine to reach the blood and lymph streams.

In humans, the tube is divided into two parts, called the small and large intestines. They are given these names because of their different widths, not their lengths. The small intestine is about 3.75 cm [1.5 in] across at its widest point. The large intestine reaches a width of about 6.25 cm [2.5 in]. The small intestine is about 6.6 m [22 ft] long, but the large intestine is about 1.8 m [6 ft] long.

The small intestine starts at the stomach. Its first part is the duodenum. This receives partly digested food from the stomach, through a ring of muscle called the pyloric sphincter, which acts as a valve. Into the duodenum lead ducts from the liver and the pancreas.

The duodenum leads into the middle part of the small intestine, which is called the jejunum. The jejunum is connected to the beginning of the large intestine by the last part of the small intestine, the ileum. The first few centimeters of the large intestine are called the cecum. Attached to the cecum is the narrow fingerlike tube called the appendix. The cecum leads into the colon, which forms the greater part of the large intestine.

The colon extends in a big loop, up the right-hand side of the abdomen, across the front, and down the left-hand side. From here it leads into the rectum, which passes downward through the pelvis. The final part of the large intestine is the anal canal, which opens to the outside at the anus.

The wall of the intestine is in several layers. The innermost layer is called the mucosa. It contains cells that secrete mucus and digestive juices. Outside are layers of muscle, and outside these is a slippery coat that allows loops of intestine to move past each other. The different parts of the intestine have different linings, because they have different kinds of work to do.

The duodenum receives food that the stomach has started to digest. It makes its own digestive juices from the mucosa. It also receives juices from the nearby gland called the pancreas. The digestive juices contain enzymes that break down food. (*See* ENZYME.)

In the following parts of the small intestine, the jejunum and the ileum, food materials are absorbed into the bloodstream. Tiny branching fingerlike projections absorb the glucose and amino acids and pass them into the blood. Fatty acids are also absorbed. They pass into the lymph stream, and eventually into the bloodstream also. The projections from the mucosa are called villi. They increase the area through which food materials can be absorbed by many hundreds of times.

By the time the contents of the small intestine reach the large intestine, most of the food material has been digested and absorbed. All that remains is undigested food, worn-out cells from the mucosa, dead and dying bacteria, used digestive juices, and water.

In the colon, water is absorbed from the remaining contents and is taken into the bloodstream. By the time the contents reach the end of the colon, they are semi-solid. The thick material is called feces. The feces are stored in the lower part of the colon and the rectum until it is convenient to discharge them to the outside through the anus. From the beginning to the end of the intestine, the contents are pushed along by the muscular intestinal walls. *See also* DIGESTION; LIVER; PANCREAS; STOMACH.   D.M.H.W./J.J.F.

INVENTION (in ven' chən) Invention means the production of something new.

History of Inventions

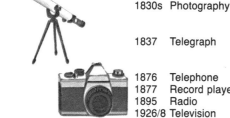

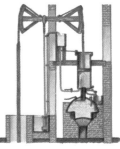

INDUSTRY

1698	Steam Pump	Thomas Savery (Britain)
1712	Beam Engine	Thomas Newcomen (Britain)
1733	Flying Shuttle	John Kay (Britain)
1767	Spinning Jenny	James Hargreaves (Britain)
1780s	Double-acting steam engine	James Watt (Britain)
1790s	Cotton Gin	Eli Whitney (USA)
1800	Lathe	Henry Maudsley (Britain)
1839	Steam Hammer	James Nasmyth (Britain)
1856	Bessemer Steel Making Process	Henry Bessemer (Britain)
1867	Dynamite	Alfred Nobel (Sweden)
1896	Steam Turbine	Charles Curtis (USA)
1930	Cyclotron	Ernest Lawrence (USA)
1939	Digital Computer	Howard Aiken (USA)

TRANSPORT

Year	Invention	Inventor
1801	Steam Locomotive	Richard Trevithick (Britain)
1837	Screw Propeller	John Ericsson (Sweden)
1877	Four Stroke Internal combustion engine	Nikolas August Otto (Germany)
1885	Gasoline (Petrol) engine	Karl Benz and Gottlieb Daimler (Germany)
1888	Pneumatic Tire	John Dunlop (Britain)
1893	Diesel engine	Rudolf Diesel (Germany)
1903	Powered Airplane	Wilbur and Orville Wright (USA)
1937	Jet Engine	Frank Whittle (Britain)
1955	Air Cushion Vehicle	Christopher Cockerell (Britain)

COMMUNICATIONS

1450	Movable Printing Type	Johannes Gutenberg (Germany)
1608	Refracting Telescope	Hans Lipershey (Holland)
1811	Mechanical Printing Press	Friedrich Koenig (Germany)
1830s	Photography	Joseph Niépce (France)
		Louis J. M. Daguerre (France)
		William Fox Talbot (Britain)
1837	Telegraph	William Cooke (Britain)
		Charles Wheatstone (Britain)
		Samuel Morse (USA)
1876	Telephone	Alexander Graham Bell (USA)
1877	Record player	Thomas Alva Edison (USA)
1895	Radio	Guglielmo Marconi (Italy)
1926/8	Television	John Logie Baird (Britain)
		Vladimir Zworykin (USA)
1948	Transistor	William Shockley, John Bardeen, W. H. Brattain (USA)
1958	Laser	Arthur Schawlow, Charles Townes (USA)

MEDICINE

Year	Invention	Inventor
1590	Compound Microscope	Zacharias Janssen (Holland)
1593	Thermometer	Galileo Galilei (Italy)
1816	Stethoscope	René T. H. Laenec (France)
1842	Anaesthetic pad	Crawford Williamson Long (USA)
1867	Antiseptic spray apparatus	Joseph Lister (Britain)
1895	X Ray machine	Wilhelm Roentgen (Germany)
1928	Penicillin	Alexander Fleming (Britain)
1982	Artificial Heart	Robert Jarvik (USA)

DOMESTIC

Year	Invention	Inventor
1845	Sewing Machine	Elias Howe (USA)
1852	Safety Elevator (Lift)	Elisha Graves Otis (USA)
1867	Typewriter	Christopher L. Sholes (USA)
		Carlos Glidden (USA)
1879	Electric Light	Thomas Alva Edison (USA)

Humans' inventions have given them power over their environment. They help humans have better, easier, and happier lives.

An invention is different from a discovery. A discovery happens when something that is present in nature is seen or known about for the first time. An invention, on the other hand, is the making of something that was never present before. For example, humans discovered fire. But someone invented the match to start a fire. An invention happens when a person puts knowledge and skill together to make use of discoveries.

Although most inventions have helped humans, some, such as weapons of war, have caused harm. Other inventions have been both helpful and harmful. The automobile, for example, is a great means of transportation. But it has also added greatly to air pollution.

Before the 1900s, most inventors worked alone. Many of them had little schooling. Today, teams of engineers and scientists, who work together in laboratories, come up with most inventions.

The table lists some of the important inventions of the past 500 years. It includes the invention of the printing press by Johannes Gutenberg in Germany. The Chinese really invented printing many years before Gutenberg's time. But Gutenberg's machine led to the printing of books, magazines, and newspapers.

The Chinese invented a great many things. The list includes paper, gunpowder, rockets, and the spinning wheel.

Some inventions changed history. The Industrial Revolution came about because of the invention of spinning machines (for making cloth), and steam engines to drive them. The atomic bomb of World War II marked the beginning of the ''Atomic Age'' we now live in.

One of the greatest inventors in history was probably America's Thomas Alva Edison. He came up with more than a thousand inventions, including the electric light, the phonograph, and movies with sound. Edison spent many hours every day of his life working on inventions. He once said that genius is ''one percent inspiration, and 99 percent perspiration.'' *See also* EDISON, THOMAS ALVA.
W.R.P./R.W.L.

INVERSE SQUARE LAW (in' vərs skwar' lö) The inverse square law is a way of calculating how light, heat, and sound are affected by distance. If you are standing three feet away from a fire, and move nine feet away, you have increased the distance three times. You might think that you would, therefore, receive one third as much heat. This is not so. The inverse square law says that you receive only one ninth as much heat. You must take the square of the distance to calculate the difference.

In the same way, we can calculate how much light reaches the planet Pluto. Pluto is 400 times farther away from the sun than is the earth. The square of 400 is 160,000. To an astronaut on Pluto, the brightness of the sun would be 1/160,000th of the brightness seen on earth.

The inverse square law applies to all forms of energy that work at a distance. However, it only applies if the source is small compared to the distance between the source and its observer. Light, heat, X rays, radio waves, sound waves, magnetism, and gravity are all ruled by the inverse square law.
D.M.H.W./A.I.

INVERTEBRATE (in vərt' ə brət) An invertebrate is an animal without a backbone or other skeleton inside the body. (*See* SKELETON.) More than 90 percent of all animal species are invertebrates. Some are so small that they can be seen only under a microscope. Others are huge, like giant squids.

Many invertebrates have no skeleton at all. They must depend on the weight of body fluids to give them shape. Some invertebrates have tough skeletons called exoskeletons on the outsides of their bodies. (*See* AR-THROPODA.) Other invertebrates have hard, thick shells. (*See* MOLLUSCA.) *See also* VERTEBRATE.   A.J.C./C.S.H.

The crane fly is an invertebrate animal that has a hard outer covering, or exoskeleton. This is flexible at the joints, and is stiff enough to hold attached muscles inside the animal.

IODIDE (ī′ ə dīd′) An iodide is a compound of the element iodine with another element. The simplest iodide is hydrogen iodide. It has the formula HI. It is also called hydriodic acid. With metals, hydriodic acid forms salts, which are also iodides. Sodium iodide and potassium iodide are metal iodides. They are found in sea water and in seaweed. Potassium iodide is added to table salt to help prevent goiter, a swelling of the thyroid gland in the neck. (*See* IODINE.)

With the element silver, iodine forms silver iodide. Silver iodide is a chemical that is used to make film. When light strikes it, it darkens. It breaks down to produce metallic silver. The black parts of a film negative contain silver that has been released from silver iodide.

With non-metallic elements, iodine forms compounds that are not so stable as metal iodides. With nitrogen, it forms nitrogen triiodide. This is so explosive that the least vibration will set it off. Iodides belong to the class of compounds call halides. (*See* HALO-GEN.)   D.M.H.W./A.D.

IODINE (ī′ ə dīn) Iodine is a non-metallic element. It forms purplish-black, shiny crystals. It has the atomic number 53, and its atomic weight is 126.9044. When solid iodine is heated, it turns into a vapor at 113.6°C [236°F]. A substance that turns from solid directly into vapor is said to sublime. When iodine is heated under pressure, it does not sublime. At 113.6°C it turns into a liquid, which boils at 183°C [361°F]. The chemical symbol for iodine is I. Iodine vapor has two atoms in each molecule. Its formula is therefore I_2. The vapor is purple in color and very dense.

Iodine is a member of the halogen family of elements. It is not so reactive as the other members. (*See* HALOGEN.) It is not found free in nature, but always in compounds with other elements. It has a valence of one in most of its compounds. (*See* VALENCE.) Iodides are compounds of iodine with one or more other elements. Hydrogen iodide (HI) is also called hydriodic acid. The iodides are salts of hydriodic acid. With hydrogen and oxygen, iodine forms iodic acid (HIO_3). The salts of iodic acid are called iodates.

Iodine is a strong antiseptic (germ killer). It can be dissolved in alcohol to form tincture of iodine. This is used to kill germs in cuts and scratches. Iodoform is also used as an antiseptic. It has the formula CHI_3. Compounds of iodine are used to make dyes and photographic chemicals.

Iodine is important to health. The thyroid gland, in the neck, needs it to make its hormones. There is normally enough iodine in the diet to stay healthy. But in some areas of the world there is very little iodine in the soil. Food grown there does not contain enough iodine. A person who does not get enough iodine may develop a goiter. A goiter is a swelling of the thyroid gland. To help prevent goiter, most table salt is now iodized. This means that a little potassium iodide is added to it.

Iodine has several isotopes that can be made in a laboratory. They are radioactive.

The most useful isotope is iodine 131. It is called radio-iodine. It can be used to treat goiter.

Chemists can test for the presence of iodine by using starch. A solution of starch goes blue when iodine is added to it. In the same way, iodine can be used to test for the presence of starch. If a few drops of tincture of iodine are put on a slice of potato, it quickly becomes blue, showing that it contains starch.

Iodine is a fairly common element. It is found in sea water, seaweed, Chilean saltpeter, brine from oil wells, and water from mineral springs. It can be taken from all these sources. It is usually found as the iodide or iodate salts. Iodine was discovered by the French chemist Bernard Courtois in 1811. He found it in seaweed.   D.M.H.W./J.R.W.

Seaweed is a source of iodine.

IONS AND IONIZATION An ion (ī′ ən) is an atom or group of atoms that has lost or gained electrons. As a rule, an atom has an equal number of electrons and protons in its nucleus. The number is the same as the atomic number. Electrons each have one negative electric charge. Protons each have one positive electric charge. The numbers of negative and positive charges are the same, so the atom is electrically neutral. But the electrons are around the nucleus and they are not bound to one another, as the protons in the nucleus are. Electrons can be lost. When one is lost, it leaves a proton in the nucleus that has no

negative charge to balance its own positive charge. The atom is left with a positive electric charge. It is now a positive ion.

Hydrogen is the simplest element. Each atom has just one proton in its nucleus and one electron. It can only lose one electron, so a hydrogen ion has just one positive charge. Larger atoms may lose one, two, three, or even four electrons. There are few ions with more than four charges. When electrons are added to an atom, they increase the number of negative charges. Negative ions are formed.

To show how many charges an ion has, chemists use plus and minus signs. A hydrogen ion is written H^+. This shows that it has one positive charge. Sometimes a dot is used instead of a plus sign. The hydrogen ion would be $H\cdot$. When chlorine forms ions, it can gain an electron. Each atom gains a negative charge. The atom is called a chloride ion. It can be written Cl^-. Instead of a negative sign, a stroke (/) can be used.

Zinc can form ions with two positive charges. This zinc ion is therefore Zn^{++}. Sulfate ions have two negative charges SO_4^{--}. Aluminum ions (AL^{+++}) and phosphate ions (PO_4^{---}) each have three electric charges. The number of charges that an ion can have is called its valence. (*See* VALENCE.) Hydrogen can only have a valence of one. But most elements have more than one valence. Manganese has six different valences. Its ions are different in the different compounds it forms.

When an element has more than one valence, different names may be used to tell them apart. Copper forms ions with a valence of one. These are called cuprous ions. Copper also forms ions with a valence of two. These are called cupric ions. In the same way, iron forms ferrous ions (valence two) and ferric ions (valence three). Another way of telling valences apart is to use Roman numerals. Ferrous ions can be written iron (II) and ferric ions written iron (III).

Ions that have opposite electric charges attract (move toward) each other. Sodium

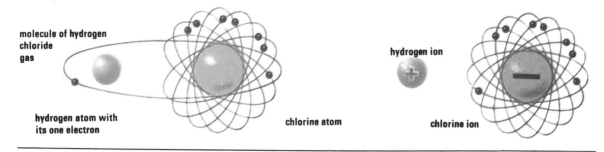

molecule of hydrogen chloride gas

hydrogen atom with its one electron

chlorine atom

hydrogen ion

chlorine ion

Left, a molecule of hydrogen chloride. Only the outermost electrons of the chlorine atom are shown. When hydrogen chloride is dissolved in water, its molecule separates into two ions, as shown right. The hydrogen atom loses its electron, becoming a positively charged hydrogen ion. The chlorine atom gains this electron, becoming a negatively charged chlorine ion.

makes a positive ion (Na^+). Chloride is a negative ion (Cl^-). This is a molecule of common salt. Molecules of compounds like this often line up and form crystals. They form a three-way pattern called a lattice. (*See* LAT-TICE.) They are called ionic compounds.

When crystals are heated, the lattice is destroyed. The ions of the compound can move around by themselves. The compound can turn from a solid into a liquid. The same thing happens when crystals are dissolved. The lattice breaks up. The ions move freely about to form a solution. They spread among the molecules of water.

If an ionic compound is melted or dissolved, it will conduct electricity. It is called an electrolyte. An electric current will pass between two electrodes dipped into the liquid. (*See* ELECTRODE.) An electrode with a positive electric charge is an anode. It attracts ions with a negative charge. Ions with negative charges are called anions. An electrode with a negative charge attracts positive ions. The electrode is called a cathode. The ions it attracts are called cations. In a solution of

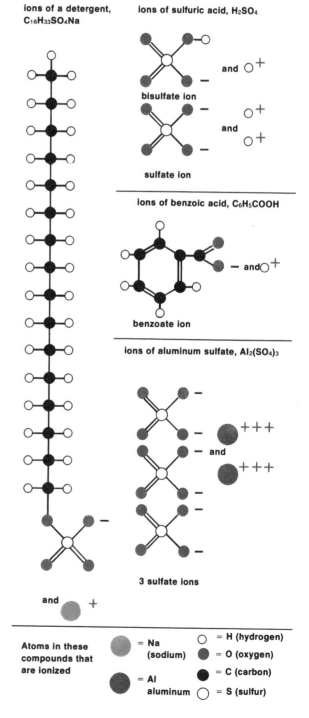

ions of a detergent, $C_{16}H_{33}SO_4Na$

ions of sulfuric acid, H_2SO_4

and

bisulfate ion

and

sulfate ion

ions of benzoic acid, C_6H_5COOH

— and

benzoate ion

ions of aluminum sulfate, $Al_2(SO_4)_3$

and

3 sulfate ions

and

Atoms in these compounds that are ionized	= Na (sodium)	○ = H (hydrogen)
	● = O (oxygen)
	= Al aluminum	● = C (carbon)
	○ = S (sulfur)

Sulfuric acid shows that a compound can ionize in more than one way. The detergent and benzoic acid molecules show that the ions of a compound can differ greatly in size and complexity. One molecule of aluminum sulfate may provide five ions.

sodium chloride, the sodium ions are the cations and the chloride ions are the anions. It is the anions and cations moving through the liquid that carry the electric current.

Ionization Ionization (ī′ ə nə zā′ shən) is the formation of ions. It happens when the molecules of an ionic compound split up into particles (tiny parts) with electric charges. It also happens when electrons are removed from single atoms of any substance. To remove electrons like this requires energy. Heat is a form of energy. When a gas is heated to a high temperature, it becomes ionized. The glowing gases that make up the sun and stars are all ionized. A gas heated until all of its atoms are ionized is called a plasma. (*See* PLASMA.)

Other kinds of energy may cause ionization. Radiation such as ultraviolet rays, X rays, gamma rays, and cosmic rays ionizes gases that it passes through. A beam of electrons will also cause ionization in a gas. Flashes of lightning are caused by electrical energy jumping from atom to atom in ionized gases in the atmosphere.

Beams of ions can be directed by magnetic fields. This is done in particle accelerators and in mass spectrometers. *See also* ELECTROLYSIS; ACCELERATOR, PARTICLE; SPECTROMETER.   D.M.H.W./J.T.

IRIDIUM (ir id′ ē əm) Iridium is a rare metal. It is much like the metals platinum and osmium. In nature it is usually found mixed with them as alloys. Iridium has the atomic number 77 and its atomic weight is 192.2. The metal melts at 2,443°C [4,429°F] and boils at 4,527°C [8,181°F]. Its chemical symbol is Ir.

Iridium is a very heavy metal. It has a density of 22.4 grams/cu cm [1,398 lb/cu ft]. It is the densest metal except for osmium. It is also a very hard and tough metal. It is used, with platinum, to make bearings for machinery, and electrical contacts. Mixed with os-

mium, it is used to make nibs for fountain pens. Iridium was discovered in 1803 by Smithson Tennant, a British chemist.

D.M.H.W./J.R.W.

IRIS FAMILY The iris (ī′ rəs) family includes about a thousand kinds of flowering plants that are perennials, blooming each year. These plants grow in hot and warm areas all over the world. The leaves are like swords and grow from bulbs or roots called rhizomes. (*See* BULB AND CORM; RHIZOME.) The rhizomes are poisonous.

There are about 300 species in the genus *Iris*. Most of these grow in warm northern areas. The flowers are often thought to be beautiful. They are made of three sets of three petals. The lower set, called falls, curves out and bends down. The upper set, called standards, curves upward into a dome. The third set, called stylebranches, covers the reproductive parts of the flower. In many species, the falls have a hairy part called a beard. The flowers range in size from 2.5 to 30 cm [1 to 12 in]. The colors also vary by species. The name iris comes from the Greek word for rainbow. The iris is sometimes called the *fleur-de-lis*, or "lily flower." *See also* CROCUS; GLADIOLUS.   A.J.C./M.H.S.

cloud cap

bearded iris

blue rhythm

IRON (īrn) Iron is a metal. It has the atomic number 26 and its atomic weight is 55.847. The metal melts at 1,539°C [2,802°F] and boils at about 2,800°C [5,072°F]. The chemical symbol for iron is Fe. This comes from the Latin word for iron, *ferrum*. Pure iron is silvery gray and shiny.

Iron is found in many places. The center of the earth is thought to be made of a mixture of iron and nickel. Compounds of iron are mined from the ground as ores. Important ores are hematite and magnetite (iron oxides), siderite (iron carbonate), and iron pyrites (iron sulfide). Long ago, humans found that iron could be taken from its ores by heating them. Today we use great furnaces to heat the lumps of ore. This is called smelting. The furnaces are called blast furnaces.

When iron ore is smelted, it is mixed with coke, made from coal, and limestone, a rock. Most parts burn away from the ore, leaving iron. The iron is almost pure. The other things that are mixed with the iron are carbon, silicon, manganese, phosphorus, and sulfur. This form of iron is called cast iron, or pig iron. Cast iron is very hard. It is brittle; that is, it breaks quite easily, because of the high carbon content. Cast iron is used to make stoves, pipes, radiators, and machine parts.

Cast iron is made less brittle by further heating. This gets rid of some of the carbon. When the iron contains 3 percent carbon and one percent silicon, it is more malleable. This means that it can more easily be beaten and worked into different shapes. It can be used to make farm machinery and tools.

Iron can be made purer still by a puddling furnace. This has a special lining. The furnace reaches a very high temperature. Most of the impurities are burnt away. The iron that is produced is called wrought iron. Wrought iron is malleable. It is used to make chains, anchors, water pipes, and many other things. The purest iron is made by electrolysis. (*See* ELECTROLYSIS.)

Steel is iron with a little carbon and other things mixed in. There are many kinds of steel. Low-carbon steel contains only 0.05 percent carbon. High-carbon steel contains up to 1.5 percent carbon. Stainless steel contains about 12 percent chromium. This stops it from rusting. Other steels are made with manganese, nickel, and tungsten.

Iron forms two series of compounds. In ferrous compounds, it has a valence of two. In ferric compounds it has a valence of three. (*See* VALENCE.) Ferrous salts are often pale green, and ferric salts are brown. The rust that forms on iron is mainly ferric oxide. Molecules of water are part of it. Iron compounds are used to make pigments, matter used in coloring, and inks. They are also used to

Below, molten iron flows down a trough.

Top, an early iron bridge. Above, an iron locomotive of the 1800s.

Below, a crushing plant at an iron ore mine.

make cloth and film for cameras.

We need iron to stay alive. The corpuscles of our blood contain hemoglobin. This is a red coloring that contains iron. It carries oxygen from the lungs to the whole body. We get enough iron in most of our food. Lack of iron leads to the disease anemia. People with anemia may be given iron compounds.

Iron is strongly magnetic. Materials that are as magnetic as iron are said to be ferromagnetic. The magnetism of iron is useful in the making of all kinds of electrical machinery. Magnetic iron oxide is used to make the tapes for tape recorders and computers. *See also* STEEL.   D.M.H.W./J.R.W.

IRON AGE (īrn āj) The Iron Age was the time in history when people used iron for weapons and tools. It began about 1200 B.C. in the Near East and southeastern Europe. The use of iron did not spread to northern Europe until Roman times. In China the Iron Age began about 600 B.C.

The Iron Age is thought of as the third of the three great ages after the Stone Age and the Bronze Age. Until the Iron Age, metal cost too much to be used by most people. The ancient Greek poet Homer compared the value of iron to gold. But then humans found that there was much iron ore. This made iron cheaper than other metal. Craftsmen began making tools, weapons, coins, and even farm tools, such as plows, out of iron. The increase in trade and communication, in part due to the use of iron, was important to the growth of civilization. *See also* IRON.   J.M.C./W.R.S.

IRRADIATION (ir ād' ē ā shən) Irradiation is the process of exposing things to radiation. The radiation may be of two basic forms. Corpuscular radiation is a stream of high-speed nuclear particles, such as neutrons, protons, electrons, and alpha particles. Electromagnetic radiation is in the form of rays, such as gamma rays, ultraviolet rays, or X rays.

Uncontrolled amounts of radiation can be dangerous to human beings. But controlled amounts are often helpful. For example, carefully controlled radiation can kill cancerous tissue. The gamma radiation given off by the radioactive isotope cobalt-60 is commonly used for this purpose. Treatment of disease by means such as X rays or radioactive substances is called radiotherapy.

Uncontrolled amounts of radiation can be harmful not only to human beings, but to any living thing. Radiation is deadly to bacteria and insects. Scientists have found that certain foods can be preserved for months by treating them with gamma rays to kill decay-producing bacteria. In grain storage elevators, insect pests are sometimes killed by irradiation. Sometimes irradiation is used in insect control to sterilize the males. When this is done, the insects can no longer reproduce.

Radiation also produces mutations in the genes which carry the traits of life from one generation to the next. Irradiation methods have been used to produce helpful mutations in certain plants. For example, the process has been used on rice and wheat to produce hardier, higher-yielding, or earlier-ripening strains. *See also* GENETICS; FOOD PRESERVATION; RADIATION.   J.J.A./J.D.

IRRIGATION (ir' ə gā' shən) Irrigation is the watering of land to make it better for farming. Irrigation is usually done in places that do not receive enough rainfall to grow crops.

Humans have irrigated land for thousands of years. The ancient Egyptians used water from the Nile River for irrigation. The Romans built great aqueducts, ditches raised above the ground, to carry water where it was needed.

Land is irrigated in many different ways. A natural spring may provide enough water for a small farm. In some places, the land is irrigated by ground water that is pumped to the surface. (*See* GROUND WATER.) Lakes called reservoirs are made by building dams to hold back water that would otherwise flow to the sea. The Aswan Dam in Egypt provides water for great stretches of dry land.

Many farmers in the United States and Canada make ditches between rows of crops. The amount of water allowed to flow through the ditches depends on the crop being grown.

Irrigation also plays an important part in conservation. When not enough rain falls, farmers cannot grow crops. The soil becomes dry, and wind blows it away. Irrigation can stop this and crops can be grown with little or no rain.

Irrigation may someday make it possible for everyone to have enough to eat. More and more land that was once not good for farming is now irrigated, fertile farmland. Countries with large areas of irrigated land include the United States, Russia, Egypt, Italy, France, Spain, Mexico, and Iraq. *See also* AGRICULTURE; CLIMATE; DROUGHT.   J.M.C./F.W.S.

Modern methods of irrigation have made it possible to grow food in previously dry areas.

ISOBAR AND ISOTHERM Isobars (ī′ sə bärz′) are lines on a weather map that connect places of equal barometric pressure, that is, the pressure of air upon the earth's surface. Isotherms (ī′ sə thərmz′) are lines on a weather map that connect places with equal temperature.

Isobars are an important aid to weather forecasting. Meteorologists, persons who study and forecast weather, can use them to predict storm movements and wind direction.

In North America, isotherms tend to curve up and down. They show differences in temperature at places of the same latitude. (*See* LATITUDE AND LONGITUDE.) Meteorologists can use isotherms to locate weather fronts, along which storms often lie, as well as to forecast temperatures. *See also* METEOROLOGY; WEATHER.   J.M.C./C.R.

ISOMER (ī′ sə mər) Isomers are groups of chemical compounds. The molecules of the different compounds are built from the same numbers and kind of atoms. However, the atoms are arranged differently and, therefore, the structure of the molecules is different. As an example, think of making a molecule from two carbon atoms, six hydrogen atoms, and one oxygen atom. One way of arranging the atoms is the shape:

$$H-\overset{\overset{\displaystyle H}{|}}{\underset{\underset{\displaystyle H}{|}}{C}}-\overset{\overset{\displaystyle H}{|}}{\underset{\underset{\displaystyle H}{|}}{C}}-O-H$$

This makes a molecule of ethyl alcohol, or ethanol. Another way of arranging them would be:

$$H-\overset{\overset{\displaystyle H}{|}}{\underset{\underset{\displaystyle H}{|}}{C}}-O-\overset{\overset{\displaystyle H}{|}}{\underset{\underset{\displaystyle H}{|}}{C}}-H$$

This makes a molecule of dimethyl ether. Ethanol and dimethyl ether are isomers.

Isomers are very common in organic

compounds. Organic compounds contain carbon atoms, often linked together in chains. The chains may be straight or branched. There are many ways of arranging the same atoms. The more carbon atoms there are, the more possible isomers there are. Most of the long-chain isomers have similar properties. There are several different kinds of isomers.

Structural isomers have simple differences in shape. Butane and isobutane are structural isomers. They both have the formula C_4H_{10}. Normal butane has its four carbon atoms in a straight line. In isobutane the carbon atoms are arranged in a T-shape:

normal butane   isobutane

Stereoisomers have groups of atoms in different places in their molecules. Maleic and fumaric acid are stereoisomers. They both have two –COOH groups of atoms. In fumaric acid the groups are on opposite sides of the molecule. In maleic acid they are on the same side. In cases like this, when the groups are on the opposite sides the isomer is called the trans form. When they are on the same side, the isomer is called the cis form. This

kind of isomerism is also called cis-trans isomerism, or geometric isomerism.

Optical isomers have molecules that are mirror images of each other. They differ in the way a left-hand glove differs from a right-hand glove. When a beam of polarized light is passed through a solution, the light is rotated. It rotates either clockwise or counterclockwise, depending upon which optical isomer is present. To distinguish them, the isomers are called d- or dextro (right-handed), and l- or laevo forms (left-handed). (*See* POLARIZED LIGHT.)

Tautomerism is another kind of isomerism. Tautomers may be changed into one another by a movement of atoms in the molecule. They exist together in equilibrium. If one of the forms is taken away from a mixture, some of the other form will change to replace it. The balance of the mixture will be restored.   D.M.H.W./J.M.

ISOSTASY (ī säs′ tə sē) Isostasy is the equilibrium, or state of balance, of the earth's crust. C. E. Dutton brought out the isostatic theory in 1889. According to the theory, the rocks of the earth's crust ''float'' on the plastic (non-rigid) rocks of the earth's mantle. Where these crustal rocks are thickest and least dense, they float highest and form continents. The thinner, denser crustal rocks float lower, forming the ocean floors. Move-

On the left, maleic acid with the acid groups on the same side of the molecule (the cis isomer). On the right, a fumaric acid molecule with the acid groups on opposite sides (the trans isomer).

Below, optical isomerism. Lactic acid can exist in two isomeric forms, the molecules of which are mirror images of one another. Optical isomers have carbon atoms bonded to four different groups.

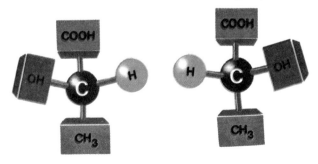

ments of the earth's crust are thought to keep the isostatic balance. It is also thought that mountains have "roots" below the surface that balance their mass above the surface.

Isostatic balance can be disturbed. For example, the melting of a large area of ice reduces the mass above the surface. The land must rise to keep isostasy. The land in the Arctic region is still rising about 1 m [39 in] every one hundred years as a result of ice sheets that melted during late Pleistocene epoch, which ended about 500,000 years ago. *See also* GLACIATION; MOUNTAIN.

J.M.C./W.R.S.

ISOTOPE (ī sə tōp) Isotopes are different forms of the same element. They have different atomic weights. All the atoms of an element have the same atomic number. This is the number of protons in each nucleus. But the number of neutrons can vary. The total number of protons plus neutrons in the nucleus is called the mass number. The mass number determines how heavy each atom is. It gives the atomic weight.

Nearly all elements are mixtures of isotopes. Chlorine, for example, is a mixture of two isotopes. One has a mass number of 35. The other has two extra neutrons. It has a mass number of 37. There are different amounts of the isotopes in the mixture. The atomic weight of chlorine is an average for the mixture. It is 35.453.

Isotopes are identified by writing the mass number before or after the chemical symbol. The isotopes of chlorine can be written ^{35}Cl and ^{37}Cl, or Cl-35 and Cl-37. The isotope uranium -235 can be written U-235 or ^{235}U. Several elements exist as one isotope only. Gold is entirely Au-197, for example, and fluorine is entirely Fl-19. Other elements are mixtures with more of one isotope than the others. Bromine is an exception. It is a very nearly equal mixture of Br-79 and Br-81.

Hydrogen is the only element that has different names for its isotopes. Hydrogen with mass number l is called simply hydrogen or, sometimes, protium. The isotope with mass number 2 is called deuterium, or heavy hydrogen. Hydrogen-3 is called tritium. Tritium does not exist naturally. It is an artificial isotope.

Some natural isotopes are radioactive. (*See* RADIOACTIVITY.) Radioactive isotopes decay into the isotopes of other elements as they give off radiation. The isotopes they become may also be radioactive and decay further. Eventually an element is produced that is not radioactive. Uranium-238 is radioactive. It decays through a series of 13 other radioactive isotopes and ends up as stable lead. This process takes billions of years.

Uranium-238 is the heaviest natural isotope. However, heavier radioactive isotopes may be made artificially. This is done by bombarding atoms of heavy elements with neutrons and other particles. It is carried out in nuclear reactors and particle accelerators. In the same way, radioactive isotopes of the lighter elements may also be made. They have many uses. (*See* RADIOISOTOPE.)

In chemical reactions, the isotopes of an element behave identically. This is because the chemical properties do not depend upon the neutrons in the nucleus of each atom. They depend upon the electrons outside the nucleus.

The isotopes of an element can be separated because they have different masses. If the mixture of atoms is accelerated by some means, the lighter isotope atoms will move faster than the heavier ones. Atoms can be accelerated by means of a centrifuge. A centrifuge spins the particles at tremendously high speed. The isotopes become separated. Beams of isotopes may also be split into heavy and light atoms by electric and magnetic fields. (*See* MASS SPECTROGRAPH.) Another method is to allow a gas containing different isotopes to diffuse through porous screens at different rates. This is like sieving the gas. *See also* ACCELERATOR, PARTICLE; ELEMENT; HALF LIFE. D.M.H.W./A.I.

JACARANDA (jak′ ə ran′ də) Jacaranda is the name for some kinds of shrubs and trees that grow in warmer parts of North and South America. The wood of the jacaranda is heavy and smells sweet. These trees are popular for planting in warm places. But they cannot live in colder areas.

The fern-tree jacaranda (*Jacaranda ovalifolia*) is a tall, colorful tree often found in the southern United States. The fern-tree jacaranda has tiny leaves in bunches. These look like fern leaves. The tree sheds in early spring. In late spring, the fern tree jacaranda has large bunches of bluish purple flowers. J.J.A./M.H.S.

JACKAL (jak′ əl) The jackal is a wild, doglike animal that lives in Asia, Africa, and some parts of Europe. Because of its sad cry and its yapping, the jackal is sometimes called "the howler." Jackals are mainly scavengers. That is, they feed on animals they find dead. For this reason, they are valued as "street cleaners" in some Asian and African cities. But jackals also hunt for themselves, eating anything from insects to small antelope. Jackals also eat fruit. The animals have been known to damage bushes and trees on which fruit grows.

The common jackal (*Canis aureus*) looks like a small wolf or coyote. It stands about 36 cm [14 in] at the shoulder. Its length measures from 61 to 76 cm [2 to 2.5 ft]. It has a grayish yellow or brown coat, and a bushy tail. The black-backed jackal (*Canis mesomelas*) lives in Africa. This animal is valued for its rich, pretty fur. J.J.A./J.J.M.

The jackal, above, is a relative of the dog.

JADE (jād) Jade is a hard, tough stone. It is often used to make jewelry and carved ornaments. There are two kinds of jade—one made up of the mineral jadeite and the other of the mineral nephrite.

Nephrite is most often the source of jade. Nephrite deposits have been found in New Zealand and North America, especially in Alaska and Wyoming. Nephrite is translucent (allowing light to pass through) to dark and dull in color. The most valuable kind of nephrite is a dark green jade called spinach jade.

Jadeite is not often found. It is mined mainly in Burma and China. Jadeite comes in beautiful colors, such as light green and lilac. The best jadeite is quite valuable.

Jade minerals are often carved into delicate patterns and thin implements.

J.J.A./R.H.